THE
TREASURE CHEST
OF
MY BOOK HOUSE

EDITED BY

OLIVE BEAUPRÉ MILLER

PUBLISHERS

THE BOOK HOUSE for CHILDREN
CHICAGO

25

CONTENTS

Exploring The Wilderness
The Story of Daniel Boone
OLIVE BEAUPRÉ MILLER

IN a little rude log cabin which trailed its line of smoke above the frontier forests and patches of new-cleared field that dotted the Schuylkill Valley in the wilds of Pennsylvania, Squire Boone and his Quaker wife, Sarah, welcomed the birth of a son in 1734. A sturdy child was Daniel. Even as a small boy, he would take a knob-rooted sapling and go out hunting in the forest and when he was only ten, his father gave him a rifle. His job was to tend the cattle, to help his father with blacksmithing or work at the looms weaving "home-spun"; but always he was most apt at making or mending anything that pertained to traps or guns. Readin' and writin' and 'rithmetic were somehow crammed into his head in the poor country school of the district; but too often he played hooky, answering the call of the forest and the lure of his beckoning gun.

Through green, undulating hills around his father's farm, far into woodlands and mountains, he wandered exploring the country, tramping on long, lonely trails into dark depths of the forest, or climbing to some high hill-top for a birds-eye view of the world. Sometimes he fell in with Indians; but thanks to the generous dealings of William Penn with the red skins and the kindness accorded to them by the Quakers of Pennsylvania, these Indians were always friendly. Daniel studied their traits, their habits and their customs. When he had reached sixteen, there was no better backwoodsman in all Eastern Pennsylvania.

But now Squire Boone decided to leave his present farm and go to the Yadkin Valley in the colony of North Carolina, a very rich farming section and a paradise for game. There were eleven children in his family now. Some of these were married; but the choice land in Pennsylvania had all been taken up, leaving small chance for newly-weds to get a start on a farm; so the majority of the Boone family decided on North Carolina.

Stowing the women and children in canvas-covered wagons, the men and boys rode horses, driving the lagging cattle; and so the picturesque caravan slowly found its way to the ford at Harper's Ferry, thence up the beautifully wooded, green valley of the Shenandoah. By night they pitched their camps beside some gurgling spring and gathered their animals safely within the circle of wagons, always posting a sentinel against the possibility of surprise-attack by the Indians. Then sitting around the camp-fire, they ate their evening meal and discussed events of the day. Thus in time, they reached the Promised Land of the Yadkin, a broad expanse of prairie with luxuriant growth of grass. Here was grazing for cattle; here were fish and game with wild fruit in abundance; and off to the westward, mountains cast long purple shadows, inviting speculation concerning those untamed regions over the rim of the world.

Here in this land of plenty Squire Boone erected his cabin, and here in new country Daniel set off again exploring. Sometimes with three or four men he hunted the buffaloes which were so soon to withdraw before the advance of the white man. He hunted deer and bear. From sunrise to sunset in autumn a man could shoot bears enough to get a ton of bear-bacon for family use in winter. Wild turkeys were easy prey; beavers, otters, muskrats, panthers, wolves and wildcats abounded in the country. And so the tall young hunter, sinewy, clad in buckskin, often lay at full length behind a fallen log, his finger on the trigger, his eyes and ears alert, his thin lips tight compressed, as he tensely waited for game. Plunging through underbrush, he leapt from rock to rock across a mountain stream or climbed the rocky ridges of that bristling mountain wall. Twenty miles away at the nearest market-town good prices were paid for skins, which were regularly shipped from there to towns along the Atlantic. No one enjoyed more than Daniel the out-door life of the hunter.

When the youth was about nineteen he went out one night to hunt. He and a friend of his, both of them riding horseback, set out after deer, intending to catch the animals by the method called "shining the eyes." The friend rode on in advance, bearing on his shoulder a pan full of blazing pine knots which cast a bright, flickering glare through the dark trees of the forest. At some distance Daniel followed, his rifle prepared for action. Any deer in the thicket, awakened by the cavalcade, instead of fleeing that brilliance, would be charmed into motionless stupor and stand with eyes fixed on the light, while the hunter shot at his prey.

As the two young men went along on the edge of a farmer's field, Daniel suddenly saw two eyes shine out of the darkness. Giving the signal at once that his comrade should stop with the light, Daniel dismounted quickly and advanced under cover of bushes to come within shooting distance. He had his gun to his shoulder, his gaze firmly fixed on the eyes, when suddenly the eyes vanished and an instant rustling of underbrush told him his game had fled. That was a strange thing to happen. Never before had Daniel seen a deer escape! Rushing off in the direction where he had heard the rustling, Boone pursued his prey, but the fugitive knew the country better even than Boone and was very fleet of foot. Leaping lightly along, a shadow skirted the field fence, then cleared the fence at a bound. Daniel, weighed down with his rifle, his powder horn, bullet pouch and other hunting accoutrements, was forced to the slower expedient of climbing over the fence. Beyond was a farmer's yard and as Daniel got over the fence, he saw, racing through the shadows to the light that shone from the house, the outline of the game which he had been pursuing.

His heart gave a throb and stood still! It was a girl he was chasing, a girl whose eyes he had shined! Hurrying on to the house past a dozen barking dogs, he burst in the door of the cabin to see a girl of sixteen, frightened and panting for breath while her brother, a boy of seven, cried to the father of the family:

"Sister went down to the river! A panther came along and chased her and she's scared a'most to death!"

Energetically offering apologies, young Boone introduced himself. The handsome, ruddy-faced girl now observed her terrible pursuer, leaning on his long rifle, and looking at her in astonishment as he surveyed her fresh young beauty with eager admiration.

THE TREASURE CHEST

The tables were turned on Daniel. Instead of his shining a deer on that night of hunting in the forest, the girl's eyes had shined his heart and they held him bound in a spell which he could no more escape than could an innocent deer from the charm of the light in the fire-pan. Artless, child-like, kind, Rebecca was a charming creature. The tireless young hunter in deerskin, set out at once to woo her and refused to be beaten off his track until she had promised to wed him.

But now on this pleasant love story trouble suddenly broke. The Indians were on the rampage. From the Yadkin Valley north as far as the St. Lawrence, white men were roused and anxious. For many years France and England had struggled for the mastery of the North American Continent west of the Alleghenies. France had a weak chain of posts along the upper Great Lakes and down the Mississippi River, reaching as far as New Orleans. On the Beautiful River, however, the romantically lovely Ohio, French voyageurs, gay and boisterous in their long, swift-moving canoes, plying their dripping paddles to the tune of their old French folk-songs, met the determined advance of English-American colonists, who occupied the land and cut in on the fur trade.

The French planned to build a fort on land claimed by wealthy Virginians who had formed the Ohio Company for purposes of colonization and fur-trading in the West. Despite Virginia's protest, delivered by young Major Washington, whose brothers were interested in the Ohio Company, the French went on with their plans. Accordingly, young Washington went west with a band of Virginians to construct an English stockade on this disputed land at the forks of the Ohio where Pittsburgh stands today. In the Great Meadows, hard by the place, the French defeated Washington and erected their Fort Duquesne. And now the French and Indian War was certainly on in good earnest; for the Indians were up in arms, some as allies of the English and some supporting the French.

In 1755, General Braddock, just come from England, set out from the East with Washington on his staff to teach the French a lesson. In his army, likewise, were frontiersmen from North Carolina and young Boone went as a wagoner and blacksmith for the troop. The baggage-wagons of the train were all so exceedingly clumsy, heavy and overladen as greatly to impede the progress of the English-American troops. In a wild and tangled ravine only a few miles from Pittsburgh, Indians under French officers fell on the English army, making the baggage train the center of a fierce attack. The English and Americans were routed in the battle. Many drivers were killed; but Daniel, cutting the traces that bound his team to the wagon, mounted one of the horses and escaped the carnage in flight. After this battle, the Indians who were allies of the French were loosed, unchecked, to lay waste the panic-stricken frontiers of Pennsylvania and Virginia. Fortunately for Boone, they did not attack the Yadkin. When he reached home in safety, he found the place still at peace.

In the following spring, young Boone married the charming Rebecca; his father, old Squire Boone, who was now a Justice of the Peace, performing the ceremony. There was a gathering of the neighbors and a hilarious wedding feast, after which the two young people went to a little log cabin that stood in Squire Boone's

THE TREASURE CHEST

yard and set about their hard task of winning a livelihood from the soil and from the forest.

Daniel toiled like a beaver, sowing and reaping his crops, raising cattle and hogs, hunting for meat and furs, working at anvil or loom, and occasionally serving as a wagoner in one of the caravans that wound through the hills to the coast, where products of the backwoods were exchanged for salt and iron or other necessaries. And Rebecca in huge sun-bonnet and loose dress of home-made cloth, bare-foot in the summer, wearing moccasins in winter, worked as hard as Daniel.

The cabin in which they lived was a simple box of logs, reared in "cob-house" style, the chinks stuffed with moss and clay. It boasted a rough stone chimney, a door and perhaps a window. Down stairs there was only one room from which a ladder led up to a low attic under the rafters. All around the walls were driven great wooden pegs from which hung spare clothes together with flitches of bacon, dried venison and bear's meat. But the center of life in the house was the enormous fireplace, large enough to hold logs five or six feet long. Here, from the great iron crane was suspended the black iron pot where the young wife cooked her corn-mush, her pumpkins, beans, potatoes, squashes, pork, and game, while down below in a bake-kettle, laid over the glowing coals, she made her bread and corn pone or fried her meat for a change. A few pewter plates, forks, and spoons, wooden bowls and trenchers, with gourds and hard-shelled squashes to use as drinking-mugs were the sole dishes of the household, and over the fireplace on deer's horns, lay Daniel's cherished guns.

With spinning on her distaff, weaving cloth on her loom, making the family moccasins, cooking, sewing, mending, occasionally plying her hoe in the little vegetable patch, watching the dairy and the children, who began to come on apace, Rebecca Boone was abundantly busy.

13

There were many good times, however, in the backwoods of the Yadkin Valley. Neighbors gathered together on the long cold winter evenings, sitting around the great fireplace telling stories and talking, and if some one among them could play a home-made gourd fiddle, there was merry dancing and singing. In summer there were sports for the men—running, jumping, wrestling, throwing the tomahawk, contests in shooting the rifle or imitating the calls of wild birds and beasts of the forest. Though the land had, as yet, no organized law, sound public sentiment made these people a law unto themselves. They respected candor, honesty, hospitality, and good behavior; and very severe were the punishments they visited on offenders. If a man proved himself a coward, if he shirked his full measure of duty toward his family and the public, if he stole, did not pay his debts, or failed to treat women respectfully, he was either shunned by his fellows or forced to leave the settlement.

Most of the wealth of the settlers was in herds of horses and cattle which grazed in the lush, wild meadows and in droves of long-nosed swine which fed on the roots and acorns in the forests on the hillsides; and beside this, annual caravans carried off to the East, furs and skins from the animals killed by the real backwoodsmen who lived on the fringe of the wilderness.

Soon the rapid growth of the country made game much more scarce in Daniel's neighborhood. He was forced to take long hunting trips into less-frequented places. And when his eldest son James was seven or eight years old, he would take the boy along with him, partly to keep him company but mainly in order to teach him the ways of woodcraft and hunting. They would often spend days in the woods during autumn and early winter which was the deer-hunting season and when in an "open camp" a snow-storm overtook them, the father held the boy close as they lay with their feet toward the camp-fire.

Hunters in those days had two kinds of camps. When they were on the move, they had what they called "open camps," which meant sleeping on the ground, rolled up in their blankets, wherever darkness or weariness chanced to overtake them. When on the other hand, they remained for some time in one locality, they built a rude hut, or a "closed camp;" a half-faced cabin of logs, the front entirely open and the roof covered over with blankets, boughs, or the bark of trees. When the Indians were not to be feared, the hunters kept a fire all night in front of this enclosure in order to warm themselves. On a bed of dried leaves or hemlock boughs, they lay with their heads to the backlog and stockinged feet to the blaze. And often, when Boone and his son were out on one of their hunts, they stayed in such an enclosure. Daniel would carve his name and exploits on some tree. On Boone's Creek in Tennessee, he left one such inscription in his own peculiar spelling:

D Boone cilled A BAR on this tree year 1760.

Thus the Boone family lived for many years in North Carolina with only the interruption of a few years in Virginia, whither they had to flee on an outbreak of the Indians.

By 1765, however, Boone had grown very restless. North Carolina was by this time too thickly settled to suit him. Like all those adventurous souls who first plunged into the wilderness, he wanted a wilder life than was offered there in the Yadkin. For years he had dreamed of Kentucky, which seemed to men in those days an impenetrable Paradise, over the roadless barrier of savage, frowning mountains. In the French and Indian War Boone had met John Finley, another adventurous soul, who had suggested to him that they could reach Kentucky by following the ancient trail made by migrating buffaloes and tramped by generations of marauding Shawnee warriors, through the break in the mountains known as Cumberland Gap. For ten years Daniel had dreamed of that unknown land, Kentucky, and now it was much talked of by the settlers in the Yadkin. But to leave his home and family and the wife he loved so dearly for a journey so long and perilous, was no matter for sudden impulse.

First he went to Florida, intending to settle there if he found the land to his taste. From St. Augustine to Pensacola he and his men explored the new colony; but the number and size of the swamps were appalling to contemplate and there was not game enough to satisfy a hunter who scorned to kill alligators. At Pensacola, however, Boone purchased a house and lot which he thought in due time to occupy, but when he returned to Rebecca and described this new home to her, the sturdy frontier woman spurned his idea of moving into a gameless land. Therefore, Boone at last determined to seek Kentucky.

In the autumn of 1767 he set out with a friend. They crossed the mountain wall, following river valleys in search of the Ohio, then striking a buffalo trail, they traveled as far as a salt lick in the eastern part of Kentucky. Caught here in a snow-storm, they were forced to camp at this lick through all the hard cold winter. Buffaloes and other beasts came in large numbers to the lick and all the hunters had to do was to "rise, kill, and eat." But, though they were at this spot well west of the Cumberland Mountains, the explorers were not aware that they were really in Kentucky. The country was very hilly, covered with annoying briers and altogether forbidding, so the men despaired of reaching the promised land by this path and returned in the spring to the Yadkin.

But, now, in the following winter a peddler with horse and wagon appeared in the Yadkin Valley. Going from door to door, he offered small wares for sale to the settlers' wives in the district. This peddler was none other than Daniel's old friend, John Finley, fur-trader and Indian fighter, who, thirteen years before, had fraternized with Boone in Braddock's ill-fated campaign. Finley had, years ago, in the course of his trade with the Indians, descended the Ohio as far as the falls of that river where Louisville stands today. Thence, with some Indian customers, he had traveled widely in the interior of Kentucky. Boone was still grieving over the failure of his attempt to reach Kentucky when Finley knocked at his door.

Throughout that winter Finley remained with Boone in his cabin. And Daniel and his brother Squire, named for the old Squire Boone, who had by this time died, were ready and eager listeners to the peddler's adventurous stories of the country over the mountains. The two Boones resolved to try the route Finley told them of and the fur-trader promised to lead them by way of Cumberland Gap.

In May when the spring crops were in, Boone, John Stuart, his brother-in-law, and Finley started from Daniel's cabin, having in their employ as hunters and camp-keepers, three neighbors from the Yadkin—Joseph Holden, James Mooney, and William Cooley. Each man was fully armed, clad in the usual deerskin, and mounted on a good horse. A blanket or shaggy bearskin was strapped on behind the saddle, together with a camp-kettle and a store of salt and provisions, although for food on their journey the men would rely on game. Squire Boone remained behind. It was to be his business to care for the later crops of Daniel and John Stuart and he agreed to come with reenforcements for the hunters at the end of autumn when the harvesting was done.

Turning in their saddles to wave a last farewell to waiting wives and children, the men set their horses in motion. One after another, they disappeared around a bend in the road. Overhead the sun shone with the gentle warmth of spring; in a gorge where flowers ran riot, a mountain brook was babbling; and all around, the forest trees gleamed with their fresh, new green. It was a glorious morning to start on such an adventure.

But much of gloom and rigor lay before the travelers. Not many miles from home they had to leave the road and follow the scarcely discernible winding Indian paths that led along the ridges and through the mountain valleys. Scaling the lofty Blue Ridge, passing through the valleys of the Holston and the Clinch Rivers, they came at last to Powell's Valley, where lay Finley's promised trail. Mounting through Cumberland Gap, they reached in the quiet of sundown a high commanding summit. Before them they saw with delight the almost endless stretch of the green, far-spreading plains. Kentucky lay there before them. Descending the following day, they entered this Paradise.

"We found everywhere," Boone told a friend of his later, "abundance of wild beasts of all sorts. The buffalo were more frequent than I have seen cattle in the settlements, browsing on the leaves of the cane or cropping the herbage on these extensive plains, fearless, because ignorant of the violence of man."

A profound impression did the magnificent scenery and all the numerous evidences of great natural wealth in Kentucky make on the simple frontiersmen. Riding in leisurely fashion along the

"Warriors' Path," the explorers established, in June, a permanent camp by a stream which flowed into the Kentucky River. With astonishment they beheld the height of the tall, straight trees shading exuberant soil which was covered with tall grass and clover and almost totally clear from any kind of underbrush except the rich clumps of the cane-brakes. Down the gentle slopes of the hills murmured clear limestone brooks. It all seemed a wilderness paradise abundant in fish and game.

"This wilderness blossoms as the rose; and these desolate places are as the garden of God!"

So one who knew his Bible described this beautiful land, and Boone, for all his silence and natural taciturnity, cried with enthusiasm:

"Who would remain on the sterile pine hills of North Carolina, to hear the screaming of the jay and now and then bring down a deer too lean to be eaten? This is the land of hunters, where man and beast will grow to the fullness of their size."

The party now started hunting. Through summer and autumn

deerskins were in their best condition. When roughly dressed and dried they were worth about a dollar each and a horse could carry a hundred such skins the necessary distance to market. Beavers and otters were valuable, too, and were light enough to be carried, but the skins of buffaloes, bears, and elks were too bulky for horse-transportation. A few elk-hides were needed to cut into harness and straps, and bear and buffalo robes were very useful for bedding; but the men were most concerned with hunting the lighter game.

When an animal was killed, the hunter skinned it on the spot, packed the hide on his back together with the best portion of the meat, and carried it back to camp. At night he smoked the meat or got it ready for "jerking;" he scraped and cured the skins as he sat around the campfire. Then when many skins had been collected at camp, they were done up in bales, protected by strips of bark and placed high up on scaffolds, secure from bears and wolves. These months now in Kentucky were the happiest of Boone's life. The soft and genial climate, the beauty of the country and the freedom of this wild life appealed to him very strongly. Large packs of skins were ready and stored at the Station Camp with a generous supply of meat from bear, elk, buffalo, deer and wild turkey. The meat had been properly jerked for use in the winter before them and there was plenty of buffalo tallow and bear's oil for cooking grease. All things seemed going smoothly when disaster overtook the party.

This place where Boone's camp lay, probably the finest hunting field in all of North America, was a debatable land, frequently fought over by warring Indian tribes. One December evening, while Boone and Stuart were climbing a hill in one of the loveliest districts they had ever seen, they were suddenly surrounded by Indians. A large band of Shawnee horsemen, returning from an autumn hunt, fell on the two lone white men and quickly took

20

them prisoners. Then they forced the two captives to lead them to the white men's camp. There they plundered the place. They took all the skins and the meat which was to have kept the explorers throughout the rigor of winter, together with their horses and all their camp equipment. Releasing their prisoners at last, they considerately left each hunter just enough supplies to enable him to live on his way back to the settlements.

Boone and Stuart, enraged at having thus lost their year's work, together with all the equipment they had brought into the wilderness, proposed to start out at once to recover what had been stolen; but the other men determined to go back home to the settlements. After two days Boone and Stuart came up with the Shawnee braves. Secreting themselves in the bushes until the dark of night, the two white men contrived to steal up on the Indians, get back four or five horses, and make off with them toward their camp. But as they were on their way home they were overtaken by the savages and once again made prisoners. For a week they were kept in captivity, then they escaped in the dark and returned to Station Camp. There they found that Squire Boone, having harvested the fall crops, had arrived in their absence, and he had brought with him a fresh supply of traps, ammunition and horses.

Squire, Stuart, Daniel, and Alexander Neely, who had come along with Squire, decided to remain in Kentucky, but Finley and the other men left to head back home again. The four who stayed in the wilderness gave up Station Camp as being too dangerously near the contested Warriors' Path. They built another camp near the Kentucky River not far from the mouth of the Red River. From here in January Stuart went out to hunt and he did not come back again. Boone, setting out to find him, discovered the embers of a fire but no trace at all of Stuart. Nor was the man seen again. Five years later Boone came across some bones in a hollow sycamore tree beside the Rockcastle River and he recognized these to be Stuart's by the name of his brother-in-law which was cut on his powder-horn. What caused Stuart's death is a mystery; possibly he was wounded, chased to this spot by Indians and died there while in hiding. No one ever knew, but Boone very greatly missed his merry companionship.

Soon after this Neely went home, satisfied with the skins which he had won in hunting, and not long after Squire Boone was obliged to go back to the Yadkin. He must sell the skins they had gathered, pay up with the price they brought the debts incurred by the Boones in equipping this expedition and return again to Daniel with a fresh supply of ammunition. On the first day of May, a year to a day since Daniel had started from home, Squire Boone silently wrung the sinewy hand of his brother, swung himself into the saddle, and taking the horses with him, disappeared down the Warriors' Path. By remaining here in Kentucky Daniel would save time and money. He could keep things shipshape in camp, mend traps, repair the rifles, and make further explorations in the unknown land of Kentucky.

Boone himself says of this parting: "On the first of May, 1770, my brother returned home by himself for a new recruit of horses and ammunition, leaving me alone, without bread, salt, or sugar, or even a horse or dog. I passed a few days uncomfortably. The idea of a beloved wife and family and their anxiety on my account, would have disposed me to melancholy if I had further indulged the thought."

Boone traveled far and wide in his search for the beautiful and the curious, and once when he was exploring he was suddenly surrounded by Indians. Knowing that he must surrender or leap down over a cliff that fell away precipitously for a depth of some sixty feet, he chose the risk of the leap. Springing over the edge of the rock, he landed in a small sugar-maple that grew way down below. Then sliding down the tree, he ran close under the overhanging bank of the towering cliff to avoid the arrows of the Indians, finally swimming a river wholly to escape pursuit. Until the twenty-seventh of July, he stayed alone in Kentucky and then, to his great joy, his brother returned to camp.

Soon after this Boone himself set out to return to the Yadkin, intending at last to bring his family to Kentucky. But he lingered in North Carolina working his little farm for some two years and a half before he actually ventured to take his wife and eight children out to the dangers of the wilderness.

"On the 25th of September, 1773," Boone says in his biography, "we bade farewell to our friends, and proceeded on our journey to Kentucky in company with five more families and forty men that joined us in Powell's Valley, which is one hundred and fifty miles from the now settled parts of Kentucky, but this promising beginning was soon overcast with a cloud of adversity. On the tenth of October the rear of our company was attacked by a number of Indians, who killed six and wounded one man. Of these my eldest son was one that fell in the action. Though we repulsed the enemy, yet this unhappy affair scattered our cattle, brought us into extreme difficulty and so discouraged the whole company that we retreated forty miles to Clinch River."

Daniel and his family had sold their farm in North Carolina, thus burning their bridges behind them, and so instead of retreating before even such a blow as the loss of the eldest son, they took up quarters where they were, finding a deserted cabin lying empty on the Clinch River.

Meanwhile, parties of surveyors and money-grasping land speculators were swarming into Kentucky, notching the trees for landmarks and giving evidence to Indians that the hordes of civilization would soon take their hunting grounds from them. Wrought to a high pitch of temper, the Shawnees and Cherokees combined their forces to fight these invasions into their land. From Cumberland Gap to Fort Pitt, from the Alleghenies to the Wabash, a great border war was on. Log forts were erected in each of the mountain valleys and Boone for a time served as scout, carrying messages through the wilderness but at last he was ordered home to protect the settlers in the Clinch Valley. By far the most active commander in the district round about, he often led his party of well-trained riflemen to relieve some neighboring fort which the Indians were besieging. His fame spread far and wide and by the time the war was over there were few men on the border so well known as Daniel Boone.

Richard Henderson of North Carolina heard much concerning Boone. This ambitious and self-seeking man had a dream of founding in Kentucky a colony of his own whose inhabitants should look up to him and consider him their overlord as men had done in the days of Lord Baltimore and William Penn. He knew quite well that Kentucky still belonged to Virginia; but he planned to purchase the land straight from the Cherokees, who were, he asserted, its rightful owners. To raise funds for this purpose he formed the Transylvania Company, engaging Boone to go with him to make the purchase of the Cherokees. Then he gave Daniel the most important commission of his life, which was to stake out a road, the best passage over the mountains from the settlements to Kentucky, in order that the people Henderson expected to swarm into Transylvania, should have easy access to the land. Thus it was that Daniel in 1775 staked out his Wilderness Road. His brother Squire went with him and a company of "thirty guns," almost every man of whom was a trained backwoodsman and experienced Indian fighter.

Boone struck out for Cumberland Gap, crossing with little difficulty the Clinch and Powell Rivers. For some miles beyond the Gap, his task was no more difficult than to direct the path so as to avoid abrupt descents or climbs. Aside from this, all he did was to blaze the trees on the road and cut down the undergrowth. But when his hardy backwoodsmen had forded the Rockcastle River in southeastern Kentucky, they plunged into harsher regions. Here there was thick dead brushwood, through which not even the buffalo had ever penetrated and for the next twenty miles every foot of the road was won by the most painful effort. After chopping and burning their way through this tangle of underbrush, the road-makers entered a scarcely less difficult canebrake country. Courageously, with their hatchets, they cut their path through this wilderness until a beautiful land burst all at once on their sight.

"We began to discover the pleasing and rapturous appearance of the plains of Kentucky," one of the workmen said. "A new sky and strange earth seemed to be presented to our view. So rich a soil we had never seen before—covered with clover in full bloom. The woods were abounding with wild game—turkeys so numerous that it might be said they appeared but one flock, universally scattered in the woods. It appeared that nature in the profusion of her bounty had spread a feast for all that lived, both for the animal and rational world."

Their troubles and labors now forgotten, Boone and his comrades pressed forward, intending to begin a settlement, but on March 24, while they lay encamped on a Creek less than fifteen miles from their goal, they were surrounded by Indians. It had not seemed to Boone necessary to post sentinels at their camp. He had every reason to believe that since the Border War was over there would be no danger from Indians. The redmen, however, resented any advance of the white man. Their pathetic doom of extinction already lay heavy upon them.

Waiting all night in the forest, hiding behind the trees, they advanced on the camp at sunrise. No inkling of their presence troubled the sleeping white men until they were roused at dawn by a chorus of ear-splitting yells and a volley of musketry. Luckily, however, the Indians aimed too high. Only one white man was killed. Nevertheless, Boone feared that this attack was part of a general Indian plan to prevent the white occupation of Kentucky and that the assailants would soon return with reenforcements. Therefore, he ordered his men to begin work at once on a fort. Before nightfall the fort was done and the whites were securely protected by a stout square log stockade, six or seven feet high, with but one narrow opening.

Some of Boone's party fled, leaving at once for home; but Boone himself would not yield. With stubborn determination, he advanced the last fifteen miles to the spot where his road was to end. During this last advance he had another adventure. A rumble like thunder arose, and knowing well what it meant, he bade his men climb a hill. Looking down they beheld two or three hundred buffalo, lumbering along together, a sight no longer seen in more settled lands farther East.

Soon Boone and his men were busy building the fort and log town which were to be known as Boonesborough at the end of the Wilderness Road; but in 1776 when Virginia became a state instead of an English colony, the Virginia legislature organized

THE TREASURE CHEST

Kentucky County out of which the State of Kentucky was later to be formed, thus ending Henderson's schemes for a lordly estate in the end. Boone and his family, however, remained in the town of Boonesborough.

One day while they lived here, Daniel's daughter, Jemima, went out in a canoe in the company of two friends. As the girls were paddling along, they were surprised by Indians. The redskins took them captive and marched them off into the woods, threatening instant death if they faltered along the way. But the plucky girls, stifling their sobs, made the journey without faltering, secretly tearing from their clothing little bits of cloth which they fastened to thorny bushes to mark the way they had gone. Two parties set out to find them; the one commanded by Daniel containing three young lads in love with these three girls. Boone at last found the Indians and stole up on their camp, finding them cooking their buffalo meat over a blazing fire, while the girls, a short distance off, sat exhausted on the ground. Firing all together, the white men rushed into the camp, driving the Indians away and recovering the girls in safety. When they returned to Boonesborough Elizabeth Callaway, one of the rescued girls, married the youth who had saved her. There was dancing to fiddle music by the flickering light of buffalo

tallow candles in one of the little cabins and Daniel, as Justice of the Peace, performed the ceremony. Later the other two girls, including Jemima Boone, married the other two youths who had gone so stoutly to their assistance.

Boone was still living in Boonesborough when far away over the mountains in the Atlantic States, the War of the Revolution upset the history of the country. Out in the wilderness in those days Boone and his frontier companions had to busy themselves with protecting their homes from the Indians. Almost cut off from help in the mother state of Virginia, Boone was one of the foremost powers in holding the Middle West, to be, when the war was over, a part of the United States.

He was out one day in January of 1778 trying with a party to bring back much-needed salt from the salt licks in the vicinity, when he was captured by Indians and commanded to lead the band against his own fort at Boonesborough. Knowing well that the town was as yet unprepared for attack, Boone resorted to a trick. He went back home with the Indians, let them adopt him into their tribe and promised in the spring to lead them against the town. While living in their camp he pretended to be quite happy; but he was in reality learning about their intended attack. The Indians took him to Detroit where their ally, the English Governor, tried to buy Boone for the British. To avoid captivity there, Boone promised that he would surrender the people of his town and conduct them to Detroit to live under British jurisdiction. Thus he returned to his neighborhood with his Shawnee captors. But on the 16th of June, Boone escaped from the Indians, taking his life in his hands.

After four days of fast tramping, never daring to kill game for food lest the sound of his gun should betray him to the Indians he staggered into Boonesborough. There he told his people the plans the Indians had made and Boonesborough quickly made ready to put up a stubborn defense. In September the redmen came. For ten days, surrounding the city, they laid a strenuous siege. But Boone had prepared his people and the town held out so stoutly that at last the Indians, disheartened, disappeared into the forest as silently as they had come.

In spite of this bold success, Boone still had to stand court-martial on charges of those who said he had sold out his people to the British, but he defended himself with such force and sincerity in this trial, that he was honorably acquitted and advanced to the rank of Major.

When at last the war was over, and the years went slowly on, bringing more people constantly over the Wilderness Road and down into Kentucky, Boone began to grow restless and turn his eager eyes westward, still desiring land that was more unsettled and wild. He had no business sense and through his utter care-lessness in entering claims of land, he who had opened up so much territory to his country, had gained little for himself.

At the age of sixty-five, he set out for Missouri. Pioneers came on foot, by horseback, in canoes; they came from far and near, to bid this man farewell. A man of distinction he was among the border-people and they were as much affected as they saw him set out for Missouri as though he had been departing for the world beyond the grave. "Why at your age do you leave the comforts of home," they asked, "to subject yourself once again to the privations of the frontier?"

"Too crowded!" Daniel replied, "I want more elbow-room!"

Over the road he had made, the first which crossed the moun-tains and opened up the west, a steady stream of people, on horse-back or afoot, were to swarm down on Kentucky and fill up the Middle West; but there in far Missouri, still actively hunting and fishing, still exploring new lands, Daniel himself was to seek "more elbow-room" till he died.

The Boyhood of Buffalo Bill
Retold from his Autobiography

Bill Cody lived on a farm in Iowa. His father, Isaac Cody, had emigrated there while the state was still frontier. Indians slouched through the villages or loped along on their ponies and the stirring love of adventure was in his father's blood. In those days the railroad extended only as far as Port Byron, across the river in Illinois; but when in 1849 the cry went out that gold had been discovered in California, all the country went wild. Men began to swarm on this railroad out to the Mississippi and there begin the long journey in covered wagons over the Plains. Naturally Isaac Cody caught the general excitement. In 1854, when Bill was eight years old, Isaac picked up his family and headed west for Kansas. Two wagons carried household goods. A carriage was provided for the mother and the daughters. In addition, a trading-wagon was stocked with red blankets, beads, and trinkets to tempt the Indians. Thus they traveled for thirty days.

In the town of Weston, Missouri, the freight-wagons and the women were left in care of an uncle who kept a general store; but Isaac himself set out to look over the prairies of Kansas, pick out a claim for settlement and trade with the Indians from his wagon. To Bill's delight, his father took him along on this trip. Thoroughly thrilled, he saw for the first time a real log fort, the block-house at Fort Leavenworth. Cavalry dashed about in flashing saber drill; artillery rumbled thundering over the smooth parade ground; infantry marched and wheeled; and all about were true Westerners, men in buckskin clothes with coonskin caps or broad-brimmed hats—just the sort of adventurers of whom the boy had dreamed. Indians loafed there, too; Kickapoos, Pottawatomies, Delawares, and Choctaws. Bill was fascinated by all the sights he saw. And the soldiers meant business, too. These were not mere dress-parades; for off to the north and west the Indians, irritated by the constant encroachments of the white men on their hunting grounds, were threatening an attack and in Utah, Brigham Young, the leader of the Mormons, was making a powerful settlement that aimed to be independent of the United States. Moreover, the distant rumblings of the coming struggle over slavery could already be heard in Kansas. There was plenty of need for soldiers.

Bill's eyes were big with excitement. But his father was soon on his way. Climbing a hill in their wagon, the two looked down from the summit over the loveliest valley the boy had ever seen, the valley in which his father was to make their home. "Locking" the wagon wheels, they slid down a very steep slope and made their camp in the valley. The next day Isaac began to trade with the Indians about, and among the first deals he made was the purchase of a pony for Bill, a wild little four-year-old. The father told the boy he would have to break this pony himself and this adventure gave Bill plenty of thrills and spills.

But the boy made up his mind he would ride that pony or bust—and he certainly did not bust!

Looking west on the second evening, Bill beheld with excitement another frontier sight. A line of trappers with pack-mules came winding down the hillside. Bill's mother had often told him how trappers searched distant mountains, hunting for fur-bearing animals and living a life of adventure that fascinated the boy. Here they were in reality. Bill could scarcely contain himself! While some of the men sat down to work at preparing the skins, others built a great fire and began to get the evening meal. Bill watched them cook the dried venison and stared with wide-eyed wonder at their method of making bread. Taking a stick, they deftly wrapped the dough around it and held it over the coals until it was ready to eat. The boy nearly burst with joy when a pleasant-faced youth, looking up, caught sight of him standing there and invited him to share the meal.

As soon as Isaac and Bill, assisted by a few hired men, could get a log cabin up, the family came on from Weston and settled in the valley. The cabin had no floor at first, it was all one great bare room with only the ground underneath; but gradually a floor was built, partitions were erected and the women-folks made the place cozy. Bill now spent his spare time picking up the Kickapoo tongue from the Indian children of the neighborhood and listening with both his ears to tales of the wide plains beyond.

In 1856, when the boy was ten years old, his father went to Fort Leavenworth to collect pay for hay and wood which he had sold to the army. Bill went along on his pony; but as the two were returning, they saw a crowd of drunken horsemen in front of a trading-post. These men caught sight of Isaac. They knew him by reputation as a man who stood against slavery, and drunkenly crowding around him, they began to curse him. Isaac replied very calmly that he was not interested in freeing the slaves of the South but that he was opposed to any extension of slavery and wanted it kept out of Kansas. One of the men, full of whiskey, then angrily drew his knife and stabbed Isaac in the back. With the help of a friend Bill somehow got his father home, but in a few days the pro-slavers announced that they were coming to finish their work and kill Isaac. Soon after that, one night, the Codys heard that a party was already on its way to carry out this threat. The mother put a shawl around the father's shoulders and a sunbonnet on his head to disguise him as a woman. Then the family took him out and hid him in the midst of a field where the corn had grown up tall. The raiding party did not get him and for many days the Codys kept Isaac hidden there, taking food to him by night. As soon as it was safe the father was taken to Lawrence, an abolition stronghold, where for a time he was safe. But the gangsters drove all the stock off the Cody farm. They killed all the pigs and chickens. The only way to feed the family was for Bill to take his dog Turk and go out to hunt birds and rabbits. For some time the father remained away from his home in Kansas; but at the end of a year he returned mortally ill. The wound inflicted by the gangster had at last fulfilled its purpose. In the little log cabin in the valley Isaac Cody died, the first man to shed his blood in the fight against extending slavery to the Northern Territories.

Bill was eleven years old, and the only man of the family. He made up his mind at once that he must be the bread-winner. Seeking out an old friend by the name of Mr. Majors, who employed teamsters and wagoners to transport freight through the country, Bill asked for a job. Mr. Majors agreed to employ him, with wages of forty dollars and food as monthly pay.

The first job assigned to Bill was to accompany a herd of cattle destined for beef to the troops that had gone on an expedition against the Mormons in Utah. He carried this through successfully and wished to keep on with his work; but, big boy though he was, he had not yet learned to write. His mother, whom he loved very dearly, insisted the following winter that he stay home and go to school.

In the spring, however, new adventures developed. Lew Simpson was busily organizing in the interests of Mr. Majors, a "lightning bull team" for freight carrying. Long trains of mules had heretofore been carrying the supplies but Simpson had great faith in bulls. A picked bull train, he allowed, could beat a mule train all hollow when it came to a very long haul! All he wanted was a chance to prove it. And now he got his chance. It was agreed that Simpson's bulls should start on their westward course and a whole week later a mule train should follow them on the route. Whichever outfit managed to get to Fort Laramie first would be the winner in the contest. To Bill's almost frantic delight, Simpson let him join the party. The start was a big event. Men, women, and children gathered to watch the bulls amble out of the town while the "mule skinners," busy preparing for their own departure later, stopped work to jeer at the bull-drivers.

"We'll ketch you in a couple of days!" Tom Stewart, the boss of the mules, yelled out in derision. But Simpson only grinned.

The bull train easily made the first hundred and fifty miles. With lively excitement Bill saw that they were making good speed; for though the ordinary bull team did fifteen miles a day, these specially selected bulls under Simpson's command were doing twenty-five miles and doing it right along. But one day while the train was halting for the noon-day meal, one of the boys in the party shouted: "Here come the mules!"

Up came Stewart with his mules, crowing over certain victory. The mules went on ahead, their drivers in high spirits, exulting, taunting, mocking. But the journey was not yet ended. There were hundreds of miles still to go. Three hundred miles further on, the bulls overtook the mules, trying to cross the Platte River and floundering in the high water. The failure of grain supplies had told on the strength of the mules. They had had to exist on grass and so were now exhausted. Since there were no farms, no traders, no grain in this district, the race had really become a simple race of endurance, with the strongest stomachs winning.

Stewart made a bad job of crossing the raging Platte. His mules got mired in the quicksand. The more they pawed to get out, the deeper in they went. But Simpson chose a crossing below the ford Stewart had selected. He hitched enough bulls to each wagon to insure its easy progress, and the bulls on their big round bellies wallowed safely through the sand, using their legs as paddles. Thus Simpson and his bulls passed the mules for good. They easily won the race and Bill was justly hilarious.

In and around Fort Laramie the boy met the famous Kit Carson and other well-known hunters and he often stood by and watched, fascinated to see how, without a single sound, they could carry on long conversations in the sign language with the Indians.

In 1860 the firm to which Mr. Majors belonged organized the "Pony Express," the most picturesque messenger-service the United States has ever seen. The route of the Pony Express was from St. Joseph, Missouri, to Sacramento, California, a distance of two thousand miles. It ran across the Plains, through dreary stretches of sage-brush, over alkali deserts, and two great mountain ranges. Stations were built at intervals fifteen miles apart.

On this journey each rider rode the distance of three stations, exchanging horses at each. He went about fifteen miles an hour and covered forty-five miles. Bill was still pretty young, he was only sixteen; but he had earned a reputation for getting himself safely out of dangerous adventures and so he was hired as a rider.

Excitement was certainly plentiful during his two years' service with the Pony Express. One day he was leaving Horse Creek when a party of fifteen Indians jammed him in a sand ravine miles from the nearest station. They fired at him repeatedly and kept him from turning back to the station he had left; but his mount was a swift roan pony, the fastest in the stables. So he dug the spurs into his sides, and lying flat on his back, kept straight on for Sweetwater Bridge which lay eleven miles distant.

The Indians came on behind, riding with all speed after him, but Bill's pony drew ahead and he had a lead of two miles when at last he reached the station. There, however, he found that the stocktender at the station had been killed by the Indians during the preceding night. All the ponies had been stolen and driven off by the Indians, so no fresh mount remained to relieve Bill's exhausted steed. He had to urge on the same pony. All those long miles on one mount! At Plonts station he told the people what had happened at Sweetwater Bridge. Then, mounting a fresh horse, he rode on and finished his route.

By this time, stages were running where the old covered wagons and ox-teams had traveled in earlier days and Indians were often troublesome, coming down on the coaches between Split Rock and Three Crossings. A stage had been robbed recently; two passengers had been killed and the driver was badly wounded. Moreover, the red skins had often driven horses away from the stations. They lay in wait continually to rob the passing stages or the flying Pony Express. It was useless to run the Express till these depredations were stopped. Accordingly, the riders were ordered to lay off their jobs. But they had no intention of accepting idleness so easily. Organizing a party which Bill Cody joined, they rode into the Indians' country. Stage and express-drivers, stock-tenders, ranchmen from the district, they were forty men in the party, brave, determined, well-armed and everyone a good shot. The captain was "Wild Bill" Hickock, who had recently become a stage-driver. Tall, yellow-haired, a giant, Wild Bill had all the experience, the knowledge and courage needed for that kind of leadership. Bill Cody had known him before. They had once tramped a thousand miles after the bull train employing them had been burned by a Mormon raider, and Wild Bill had also ridden for the Pony Express.

Twenty miles from Sweetwater Bridge, the party found an Indian trail running north toward Powder River. By hoof prints they could see that the last horses over this road had been very recently shod, sure proof that they were stock stolen from the white men. Pushing on as fast as they could, they saw at Crazy Woman's Fork, evidence that another party had joined the thieves they were seeking. The trail was newly made; so the Indians could hardly be more than twenty-four hours ahead and plainly their number was large. When the white men reached Clear Creek they saw on the opposite bank a group of horses grazing. Horses meant Indians near. But these Indians were all unaware that the enemy was on their trail. Never before had white men followed them so far as this into their own country and so, not expecting pursuit, they had failed to put out any scouts. Quickly getting the "lay" of their camp, Wild Bill and his men discussed how they should make the attack. The Indians outnumbered the white men more than three to one. Without strategy all Bill's party would soon be without their scalps! But Wild Bill never knew fear. He ordered his party to wait until the night should fall. Then, creeping up very quietly, they were to burst forth suddenly and make a grand ride through the camp, opening fire as they rode and stampeding the Indians' horses.

Such a plan called for nerve, but the men were all full of spirit. The very danger of the enterprise made them relish it more. At Wild Bill's signal, they rushed pell-mell through the Indian camp, shooting their guns right and left! The Indians were astounded. The foe had dropped from the clouds! Bewildered and yelling, they scattered, rushing in every direction.

Having ridden straight through the camp, the white men circled about and came galloping back again, to make sure no Indians remained. The few still left by the camp-fire ran before their shots. No Indian was left in sight; but in the haste of departure they had deserted the stolen horses. And so Wild Bill and his party, exultantly driving before them a hundred recaptured ponies, rode back to Sweetwater Bridge. Soon the horses were again on the road and the Pony Express was resumed.

In adventures such as these Bill Cody spent his youth. He was a scout in the Civil War and later a hunter of buffaloes to feed  the employees of the Kansas Pacific Railway when its line was being extended out into the wilderness. In the hunting of buffaloes he acquired such a reputation that the railroad hands bestowed on him the name of "Buffalo Bill." For years he served in Indian wars against the Sioux and Cheyennes, and in 1883 he organized his "Wild West Show," bringing the life of the West in all its picturesque flavor before the eyes of the world.

THE PLAINS' CALL
ARTHUR CHAPMAN

I must ride out on the plains again,
  With a horse 'twixt knee and knee,
Where the wolves howl and the winds growl,
  And the clouds drift fast o'er me;
I must ride out on the plains once more,
On the Westland's broad and level floor.

I must ride forth on the plains at morn,
  Where the cactus flowers are,
And the lark calls, and the white walls
  Of the mountain loom afar;
I must ride out, when breaks the day—
Ride where the gods of outdoors play.

I must ride out on the plains at night,
  And smell the dew wet sage,
When the moon glows, and the late snows
  Gleam like a book's white page;
I must ride out on the plains again,
And quit this haunt of pygmy men.

39

The Adventures of Alexander Selkirk

Being a true Account of one Mr. Alexander Selkirk, Master of a Merchant-Man who was left ashore on a desolate Island in the South-Seas, where he lived Four Years and Four Months without seeing the Face of Man. To which is added a Description of the Island where he was cast; how he subsisted; the several Strange Things he saw; and how he used to spend his Time. Told from the Accounts of Captain Woodes Rogers, Sir Richard Steele and other Eminent Men, who had the Tale directly from the Lips of the said Alexander Selkirk in Person, he being further known to Fame by reason of his Adventures having furnished to Daniel Defoe the idea for writing of Robinson Crusoe.

IN the year 1704, there was cruising off the coast of Mexico an English galley, by name the Cinque Ports, 96 tons burden, 16 guns, and sixty odd men. The Cinque Ports had been a twelvemonth or more in those parts, at first in company with another vessel under Captain Dampier, on a voyage of exploration and adventure. In those days the greed of France and Spain to rule the world and crowd England out of the South Seas, made the relations of England with those countries none of the friendliest, and the British government commissioned private vessels to make war on the boats of the enemy wherever they might overtake them on the high seas. Of such sort was the Cinque Ports, and she had sailed along the rich gold coast of Spanish America, now and again running down some Spanish galleon, and meeting with sundry and divers adventures. Her commander was one Captain Straddling, a cross-grained, quarrelsome fellow, and he had serving under him as sailing master of the vessel, a certain hot-headed, independent young Scotchman, by name Alexander Selkirk, or Selcraig, as it is more properly written, son of a well-to-do tanner and shoemaker of Largo in Fifeshire, and a follower of the sea from his youth. Now Selkirk was an expert and able seaman, but from the start of the voyage he got on none too well with

Straddling. Straddling was an insolent bully. Right and left it was hot tongue and heavy fist wherever Straddling appeared on deck. Month after month, Selkirk held his temper in check—Straddling was his superior officer and he had a sailor's wish and training to obey. Yet was he one to brook domineering from no man, and now and again when Straddling rode his high horse, there was an outburst from Selkirk that threatened the gathering of a terrific storm.

As they sailed day after day and month after month, the Cinque Ports grew leaky and altogether unseaworthy, so Captain Straddling found himself forced at last to put in for fresh water and repairs at the island of Juan Fernandez, some four hundred miles off the coast of Chili. Juan Fernandez was lonely, wild and uninhabited. It was off the beaten track of commerce and was rarely visited by vessels of any kind, but Straddling had been forced earlier on the same voyage to put in there, and thither under stress of necessity he went again. During the three weeks or so that they lay to in the chief bay of the island, the differences between Straddling and Selkirk grew daily worse, till at last on the very day when the vessel was getting under way, an angry discussion arose. Hotter and hotter it grew. It is not improbable that fists as well as tongues came into play to settle the question, but, however that may be, the upshot of the whole matter was that Selkirk's temper took such furious fire, he burst out the door of the Captain's cabin and rushed up the companionway, shouting:

"Let me off this crazy vessel! Put me ashore, I say! I'll sail not a day longer under such an obstinate, pig-headed mule!"

The Captain followed his irate master onto the deck, bestowing upon him a string of like forceful compliments and bawling out:

"Down with the pinnace! Take him ashore! Off with the mutinous hound! He's turned out o' service!"

While the sailors swarmed to the small boat, Selkirk calmed

himself sufficiently to gather together certain of his belongings, and, having piled these into the pinnace, he was over the side of the galley and being rowed off to the shore almost before he knew it.

He saw before him a wild, luxuriant and yet savage coast, a mass of jagged, volcanic rock, hurled up in ages agone by some mighty disturbance of the earth and rudely piled into blocks and pinnacles. Mountains towered above, and over all rose the craggy peak of El Yunque (the Anvil) of which no man knew whether or no it would one day belch forth fire and overwhelm all that lay at its base with a mighty stream of lava. Yet Selkirk's spirit, at that moment, was as wild and untamed as that savage shore, and the fire within him smouldering, ready to flame, like volcanic fires of the earth. To such a state of mind the shore was inviting rather than forbidding. Anger and defiance buoyed him up. He held his head high and his eyes were glowing. Straddling himself had command of the small boat, and the moment its keel grated on the sand, Selkirk sprang lightly ashore, standing by with the utmost unconcern while the Captain gave orders concerning the unloading of his luggage.

The matter was carried through with the greatest dispatch and the sailors were soon bidding their comrade a sorrowful farewell, while Straddling sat in the boat and in surly fashion called them to make haste and be off.

All at once—Selkirk never knew how it came about so quickly, —out there, bobbing up and down on the swelling blue, half way back to the galley and going at a tremendous clip, he saw the small boat, loaded with men, and there alone on the shore he stood, Alexander Selkirk, alone, all alone!

In a trice with a sudden revulsion of feeling, it came over him what he had done. Anger and defiance were dead. The scales had fallen from his eyes. He knew what he had done. To stay alone on a savage shore—to hear no human voice—to see no

human face—for years, perhaps forever! He raised his voice in a cry that was almost a shriek, stretched out his arms toward his comrades and rushed to the very edge of the water.

"Come back! Come back! Come back!" he cried. The wind carried his voice away, and yet it seemed to him he heard from the stern of the pinnace where the Captain sat, a sound of mocking laughter. Even while it echoed in his ears, the men in the small boat boarded the larger vessel. All sail was set, and the Cinque Ports made off out of the bay and into the Pacific. He watched with straining eyes till her sails, a mere speck in the distance, dipped down behind the horizon, and the whole vast blue of ocean was left stretching empty and lone before him.

How long he stood there, almost in a stupor staring off to sea, he never knew, but suddenly he became aware that the stillness about him was so intense, it seemed of a truth to shriek in his ears. Thus brought back to himself, he looked about and observed that the sun was low in the sky. In a short time darkness would swoop down upon his solitude. Now he had no knowledge whether or no savage beasts abounded on the island, and he judged it to be most necessary that he find a shelter ere nightfall. Accordingly, though with weak and trembling knees, he searched along the shore. In a little ravine at no great distance back from the beach, he came upon a cave of moderate dimensions that offered a most excellent retreat and lay not far from a stream of fresh water.

Hither he dragged his belongings from the place on the sand where they had been dumped, and being now at liberty and of a mind to take stock of the same, he found he had with him a sea chest containing his bedding and a few extra articles of clothing, a firelock, a pound of gunpowder, a large quantity of bullets, a few pounds of tobacco, a hatchet, a knife, a kettle, a Bible, several books that concerned navigation, and his mathematical instruments. In provisions for the sustenance of life, he had but the quantity of two meals. It being then nearly dark, and no opportunity offering to search for food that night, he was obliged for the present to appease his hunger by consuming a share from his slender store. He then closed the entrance to his cave by means of his sea chest and laid himself down to sleep with his firelock close by his side. Several times during the night he fancied he heard growling and roaring as of wild beasts, but the darkness passed without incident and the sun rose with remarkable splendor.

It was early October, being spring in that latitude, and within the verdant little gorge where the cave was situated, all was bud and bloom and twitter of birds and gladsome play of sunlight and shadows. Selkirk, notwithstanding, had eyes for none of the beauties about him. He thought only of the misfortune, swift and terrible, that was come upon him. For days he sat moping and brooding by the sea shore, straining his eyes to catch sight of a sail. Not till the darkness of night made it impossible longer to watch, did he close his eyes, and then he slept but poorly. As to eating, he never ate anything at all till the extreme of hunger constrained him, and even then he took no care to make his victuals palatable. He ate only of the craw-fish and turtle to be found on the shore, for he felt spell-bound to the beach. Fortunately he had with him a kettle, and by patient trial he learned to get fire by rubbing two sticks together on his knees, after the Indian fashion. Sometimes he broiled the shell-fish and sometimes he boiled them, but he found nothing that he ate to his taste for want of salt to season it.

The whole island was in truth rich in natural beauties, in hills and valleys, delightful springs and leaping mountain streams, but Selkirk saw no beauty in it anywhere. To him its loneliness, its deadly stillness, made it all as frightful as some distorted vision of a dream. He only left the shore to climb up to a certain high point by the side of El Yunque, whence a gap in the trap-rock offered a still wider view of the sea. He made no count of days, he took no care of himself, of his clothing, or the cave in which he lived. All his soul was absorbed in that one thought, to watch for a sail, and he wore a beaten track from the shore to his look-out, from his look-out to the shore.

Along in November, as he slept an uneasy sleep within his cave, he was suddenly awakened by the increase of that growling and roaring as of wild beasts which had disturbed his first night on the island. It sounded somewhat between the howling of wolves and the thunderous roar of larger beasts and was of a nearness to make him hold all night, close by, his firelock. He never closed his eyes again for uncertainty but when the sun was risen and he stepped cautiously out of his cave towards the shore, there before him on the beach he saw myriads of seals that had come up out of the sea during the night. Some were in the water but more were on the land and these were moving their heads about, raising themselves on their flippers, roaring and bellowing. It being Selkirk's custom at once to go to his look-out on the beach, he approached the seals with some uncertainty as to their temper in letting him pass through. He held his firelock ready to beat them off with the butt in case they made at him, but he found them so surly and determined not to give way, that he was forced to beat a retreat before them. In a short time their numbers had so increased as others drew up out of the sea that they lined

the shore very thick for above half a mile of ground all around
the bay. It appeared this was the spot where it was their custom
to come each year and raise their young, and though seals be
usually peaceable creatures, as there came to be many young
among them, the old ones grew still more surly. Far from moving
out of the way, they would rise up on their flippers in their desire
to protect the whelps and make at a man fiercely like an angry
dog if he offered to go among them. Moreover, day and night,
they kept up a continuous noise of a hideous sort. So Selkirk
was obliged to avoid the beach and largely to keep his look-out
from the high place on the side of El Yunque, and in his present
state of mind the dreadful howlings and voices of these monsters
of the deep seemed almost too terrible to be borne. He had
been in the past not of a nature to bear misfortune calmly, and
many a time from sheer impatience and impotent inward rage
against the helplessness of his wretched lot he shook his fists and
cried aloud; and as no sail appeared day after day, he even medi-
tated casting himself into the sea. "Could the thought of man,"
he often demanded of himself, "devise a more utterly miserable
lot than life alone on a desert isle?"

And then at last one day as he was going through his sea chest
in search of some trifle or other, his hand fell upon the Bible and
he drew it forth with a strange tugging at his heart strings. God

knows how that Bible had ever come into his chest. It was nothing that he himself cherished or would have thought of putting there. It must have been his mother who had slipped it in among the linens her hands had packed with tender care, and as he drew it forth on this particular day in the midst of that lonely island, it took his thoughts with painful vividness back home. There rose before him in a flash the rolling downs of Fifeshire, green and dotted with sheep, the great gray cliffs along the shore, and nestling beneath them in the bay, the little town of Largo. At the west end of the village there was his home, his father's cozy, homey dwelling, surrounded by its garden, and there in the lattice window sat his mother knitting, looking off to sea perhaps and longing for news of him. Unconsciously his hand caressed the Bible; he climbed the height to his look-out, sat down with the book on his lap and buried his face in his hands. He could see it all so clearly. And now there rose before him, all overgrown with ivy, so peace-ful and serene, the kirk itself. He could see the light that streamed in through its stained glass windows, the congregation there in Sabbath day attire with fresh and happy faces, and over all a Sabbath air of quiet joy and calm. He could see his mother by his side, her eyes aglow with pride in him —so much she had expected from this, her stalwart son. And then he minded how during the very services in the kirk, his hot temper had led him to start a-brawling. His mother's

eyes grew dark with shame, men thrust him out by force, and on the books of the kirk he could see the record written as with points of fire: "Alexander Selkirk, having been for his indecent behavior summoned for trial before the kirk sessions on this 27th day August, 1695, did not compear, being gone away to the seas."

Yes, that was what he had done—run away from his punishment to the seas; and, worse still, not three years agone, when he was a man grown and home once more, he had been summoned again before the kirk sessions and publicly rebuked before the whole congregation for quarreling with his brothers and raising a tumult in his father's home. Suddenly his shoulders shook with sobs and all his soul revolted against that unruly temper that had caused him so much trouble all his life. Had it not been for that same temper, he would not have been here alone and miserable on a desert island. He wept as he had not done since he was a lad at his mother's knee, and in him rose the resolution strong, henceforth to bar out that beastly fault and never let it run away with him again. The tears he shed left him greatly purified and refreshed even as the earth after a thunder storm. Slowly he opened the book on his knees and read:

"They wandered in the wilderness in a solitary way; they found no city to dwell in.

"Hungry and thirsty their soul fainted in them;

"Then they cried unto the Lord in their trouble and He delivered them out of their distresses."

And again:

"The wilderness and the solitary place shall be glad for them; and the desert shall rejoice and blossom as the rose.

"Say to them that are of a feeble heart, Be strong, fear not; behold, your God will come . . . and save you."

Suddenly those words applied to him and to his need. Misery had melted the pride of a stubborn heart, and for the first time

in his life, his thoughts drew near to the Creator of the universe.
He read on and on, and with every word he read, his loneliness
diminished; hope took the place of despair and more and more
his spirit rose within him. At length with new vigor and purpose
he closed the book and strode down from the height to his cave.

Now for him everything was changed. He realized for the
first time that life on Juan Fernandez would be what he made it.
If he lived miserably, doing nothing to better his condition, and
pinning all his hope of happiness on the chance of a stray sail
making its way toward the island at some hazy time in the future,

he might waste away a lifetime in despair. Now, now was the time to conquer every adverse circumstance, live and be happy. "Behold, *now* is the accepted time," saith St. Paul. "Behold, *now* is the day of salvation."

He set to work at once. First of all he saw that he had let his cave grow filthy. He spent some time in cleaning it out and washing of clothes and bedding. As he worked he was able sometimes to whistle. Moreover it was a remarkable fact that the howling of the seals no longer annoyed him; he could even hear their voices with pleasure as furnishing a certain sense of companionship, and the change within his own spirits made him approach them in so different a manner, with such confidence and assurance that now, when occasion demanded, he could safely make his way through them. It is true loneliness and despair returned at times to tempt him, but he had henceforth always wherewithal to resist them through reading of the scriptures and thinking on the words therein set down.

Having put things in such order about his cave as they had not been in since his arrival on the island, he began next to consider the question of food. As he had been unwilling to leave the beach and living on that food the most easily procurable there, he had been eating almost nothing but turtle, till he could scarce brook the thought of turtle again. Now he arranged at stated intervals, morning and evening, to go to his look-out on the rocks, but the rest of the time he put the matter of sails out of his mind, and went about his business of providing for his natural wants. Accordingly, he traveled inland and on the heights back from the shore found a plenty of goats. Juan Fernandez, the Spanish sailor who had first discovered the island a century or more ago and given it his name, had resided there for some time, stocking the place with goats, and the wild creatures of this time were descendants of those domestic beasts Juan Fernandez left behind at the time of his final abandonment of the island. By means of his gun, Selkirk was thus able to provide himself with goat's flesh, and he perceived that the fruit of the pimento which is the same as the Jamaica pepper and has a most delicious smell, would season his meat instead of salt. He therefore soon learned to prepare victuals he could truly relish in place of the unpalatable stuff with which his indifference had been providing him. In particular he was able to make a most excellent broth. Being still, however, greatly in want of fresh vegetables, he decided to set out and explore the island in search of the same.

He found Juan Fernandez to be about thirteen miles in length by four in width, rocky and mountainous everywhere, the mountains being covered with green to the skyline, except where precipitous faces of rock formed a beautiful contrast to the luxuriant pale vegetation. Everywhere was a great profusion of ferns, there being two varieties of tree-ferns that raised their feathery heads to the height of a good-sized tree over many an overhanging crag or precipitous ravine. The steep paths up the hills were bordered by a thicket of flowering shrubs and herbs, one of the most remarkable of the latter throwing up leaf stalks eight and ten feet in height and forming with the leaves, which frequently measured fifteen feet across, a canopy under which one could easily have ridden on horseback. In several brooks at no great distance from his cave he found water cress of an excellent flavor and to his delight, he discovered growing in great profusion among the trees of the island, the cabbage palm which yields most edible leaf buds quite after the manner of the common cabbage.

In several places he came upon the ruins of huts or shelters that had probably been erected in times past by the few sailors preceding him who had spent periods of greater or less length on the island, though never before like him alone, being always in companies of three or four. He searched well in these places, but found nothing of any value left behind, save that from one he was able to procure a few nails. In the rank growth near these ruins, however, radishes, parsnips and turnips were growing. These appeared at present to be wild, but were undoubtedly offspring of seeds originally sowed by some one of the earlier inhabitants of the island. Thus provided with a welcome addition to his food supply, Selkirk returned to his cave, a spot now quiet and serene enough since the seals had long since departed.

It was now well along in February, being the close of summer. Selkirk had long since carved on a tree the date of his arrival on the island, and by computing the number of days during which he had kept no track of the passage of time, he had from then on carried on an accurate system of markings by which he was always able to ascertain the date. With autumn coming on and winter in view, he began to think of building himself a hut. Even in that genial climate where trees were green the year around, he knew that frost was common at night in winter, snow would sometimes be found on the ground and there would be much rain, therefore he felt the need of a more habitable shelter than his cave. This he desired the more especially as he had seen from his lookout in all the time he had been on the island only one sail and that far off on the very edge of the horizon, so he felt more than ever that he was like to stay years or perhaps forever in that place.

After thinking the matter over carefully he came to this conclusion —he must build his hut well back from the shore in a most sheltered and inaccessible spot, for by this time his powder was gone and he had no means of defence. He was now well satisfied that no savage beasts dwelt on the island, but he had this to take into consideration —if a boat ever did land there it was as like to hold men from whom he must flee as men into whose arms he could throw himself. He knew well enough the character of the rough adventurers who sailed those seas —buccaneers, pirates, outlaws. Moreover at this time, France and Spain being both at war with England, to fall into the hands of Frenchman or Spaniard would have been to be captured by a foe. At length he made up his mind that if a French vessel put in he would surrender, trusting the nature of the French to deal honorably by him even though he were an enemy. But if the vessel were Spanish, he would flee and hide himself and never give up, for he knew the jealousy of Spain for England was so great that it was her acknowledged policy never to let a single Englishman return to Europe who had any knowledge of the South Seas. If he were to fall into the hands of Spanish sailors they would either kill him or make him a slave to work in their rich South American mines. This much was certain then—he must build his hut where it would be a safe retreat in case of need. Therefore he climbed the rocks by an intricate path, and finding hidden high up among them a beautiful little glade on the edge of a spacious

wood, a spot most difficult to come at, and so concealed as to be well nigh undiscoverable, he selected that spot as the site for his hut.

By the exercise of much toil and patience, he then cut down with the small axe at his disposal, a sufficient number of pimento trees for his purpose. These he was obliged to join most accurately and carefully together by means of notches, having a great scarcity of nails. On the plains and small hills of the island there abounded a species of grass which grew to the height of seven or eight feet. This he cut most laboriously with his knife, and, on being dried, it proved to produce straw resembling that of oats. With this he thatched his hut. He then constructed a framework for a bed, covered it with straw and spread thereon his bed clothes, to sleep on which was a most welcome change after months of lying on the hard ground. Being still uncertain whether or no his hut was weather-proof, he hung the walls on the inside with well tanned skins of goats.

He had now for some time, since he had used the last of his powder, been presented with a new problem in the matter of procuring his goats. Being determined however to be overcome of no adverse circumstance, he one day made after a goat on foot. The creature was too fleet for him, but a young kid crossing his path, he found himself able to overtake that and seize it with his bare hands, and as he daily exercised to increase his speed, he was soon able to overtake the grown goats as well. He made after them first as they slackened speed to climb an ascent, but with gradual practice and owing to the moderate and temperate life he led, which kept him in fine bodily trim, he was at last able to run down even the fleetest goats at full speed on the level.

With the poor tools at his command, it took him many weeks to build his hut which he made of a spacious size. But this hut being complete, he found his energy by no means flagging, and ere the rainy season began he built at no great distance from it a second and smaller hut wherein he might cook his victuals.

Thus when winter came he was well prepared to meet it. The weather was never tempestuous, but there was some frost and snow, a little hail and great quantities of rain. In the larger hut he slept and passed the long periods of downpour. It had openings for windows which rendered it exceedingly light and pleasant, and over these openings in case of need to keep out the rain or cold could be dropped the goat skin coverings. Here within, he was cozy and snug enough, and he led a most orderly and comfortable life, instituting there the simple but beautiful form of family worship to which he had been accustomed in his father's home. Soon after he left his bed and before be began the duties of the day, he sang a psalm, then read a portion of the scriptures, finishing with devout prayer. Moreover he always repeated his devotions aloud in order to hear the sound of a human voice and retain his ability to speak the English tongue. The remainder of his time he occupied himself with making various articles of furniture and carving dishes and utensils out of wood, also in studying his books on navigation.

The winter offered but one incident of any importance and that was the coming up onto the beach early in July of great quantities of sea-lions. These strange creatures differ little in shape of body from seals but they are larger (being sometimes twenty feet long and of two tons weight). They have another sort of skin, their fur being shorter and coarser than that of the seal, and their heads are much larger in proportion, with very large mouths, monstrous big eyes and exceedingly heavy whiskers, the hair of which is stiff enough to make tooth pickers. These creatures stayed from July to September and were never observed during that time to go into the water but lay covering the shore above a musket shot from the water-side. But by this time Selkirk was in such good spirits that he was quite able to make his way safely through them whenever he needed to approach the shore.

With the return of spring, he found himself in a very different state of mind from what he had been the year before. When the rains ceased and it began to bud and twitter without, his heart leaped up and was glad within him. In the woods nearby the flowers appeared and there was a sort of blackbird with a red vest that came most tamely about his dwelling. Moreover, as the season advanced, there was scarcely a plant of myrtle or of a shrub with long dark bells like the myrtle, which was not inhabited by a pair of vari-colored humming birds, no bigger than bumble bees, and these little creatures whirring and buzzing over the flowers filled Selkirk with delight.

The fall before he had carefully collected seeds of the vegetables that grew in different parts of the island, and this spring he cultivated a goodly patch of ground near his hut, having no implement with which to till the ground save his knife and axe. Here he planted a garden which he kept free of weeds and in most excellent and orderly condition.

His one trouble now was that he was greatly pestered with rats, his hut being overrun with the vermin and they so bold as to gnaw his clothes and even his feet when sleeping. On considering how to rid himself of this pest, he determined to catch and tame some of the wild cats that inhabited the island. These creatures, though of a uniform yellowish gray color like the real wildcat were not in truth that creature, as might be told from their smaller size and from their tails which were thin and tapered at the end, while the wildcat's tail is bushy and of uniform size throughout. They, like the rats, were descendants of domestic creatures that had got ashore from some boat or other that had put in in times past to wood and water at the island. Nevertheless, though they were offspring of the tamest of beasts, they were

as fierce and wild as wildcats and of an agility that made them
well nigh impossible to catch, so quickly could they slip out of
one's very grasp and up into the trees. They formed their nests
in rocky crevices or hollow trees and when disturbed there, would
rise up and give fight, snarling and spitting fiercely, every hair
on their bodies bristling with rage. Selkirk, however, was able
to procure some kitlings which through patient care and feeding
he tamed, and these being grown, speedily delivered him from the
rats and kept his hut clean of the pests ever after.

Having succeeded well in taming the cats, he began also to tame
kids that he might have food within easy reach in case of need.
In this wise his hut was soon surrounded with tame creatures.

Pursuing goats up the mountainsides was by no means without danger, for the soil at any great height was very light and
shallow, the vegetation being mostly
a scrubby undergrowth, and if a man
seized hold of this to help himself up
the slope, the whole was like to give
way, come up by the roots and pre-
cipitate him down the steep. Once
Selkirk so eagerly pursued a goat that
he catched hold of it on the brink of
a precipice of which he was not aware,
the bushes having hid it from him.
So he fell over from a great height
with the goat under him and lay at
the bottom of the cliffs for a matter
of twenty-four hours before he came
to his senses—the amount of which
time he calculated by the change in
the moon since last he observed it.
Having then crawled a mile back to

his cottage, he there remained some ten days ere he was able to stir out again.

As time passed he began to be greatly troubled that, with so much using, his knife was worn clean to the heft. He mourned beyond measure the loss of so valuable and necessary an implement. One day, however, as he wandered on the beach, keeping a sharp lookout as he always did for aught that might be of use, what should he spy, half buried in the sand, but some iron hoops. Doubtless they had been cast away by some ship as altogether unworthy, but to him they were a treasure then more priceless than a shipload of Spanish gold. Taking them back to his hut, he there broke off a piece, beat it thin, and ground the edge upon stones. Thus by the exercise of a little ingenuity, he was able to provide himself with a knife.

The knife, as may well be believed, was not the only one of his belongings that wore out. In course of time his clothes did likewise. He then made himself a coat, cap and breeches of goatskin with the hair outside. These he stitched together with little thongs of leather which he cut from the skins and attached to a nail. Having a plenty of linen cloth by him, thanks to the care of his mother, he sewed himself shirts when his wore out, using the nail again for a needle, and for thread the worsted that he unravelled from an old pair of stockings. As his bedding gave way, he replaced that also by goatskins. Only with the wearing through of his shoes did he find here an article that he could not replace. Nevertheless, as he was forced to shift without them, he found his feet grow so hard, he could run anywhere, even over the sharp jagged rocks, without the slightest annoyance. Thus even the loss of his shoes remained no great inconvenience.

One day as he stood on his look-out scanning the sea for a sail (it must have been about in the second year of his solitude) he did indeed, to the joy of his soul, see a sail bearing straight for the island. Leaving all else, he stayed at the lookout, never taking his eyes off the ship, his heart beating high with hope. But as it drew well within the range of vision, he saw to his dismay that it was a high and clumsy vessel, its stem and stern built up like castles —Spanish without a doubt. Now as he had fully made up his mind rather to stay forever on the island than fall into the hands of the Spaniards, he watched until he made sure they were going to land, and then retired at once to his inaccessible retreat, where he stayed quietly, never once moving out of it so long as they remained on the island. From among the rocks he kept a sharp lookout over their encampment below, and he found the sight of human kind and the sound of their voices so agreeable even though he knew them to be enemies of a fierce and relentless kind, that he was often almost compelled to go down and join them. More than once some of the men strayed up the rocks straight in the direction of his hut, but fortunately he had built it so far beyond the distance of any easy climb that they never penetrated so far. At last, having taken aboard wood and water, they made off and Selkirk found himself once more the solitary master of the isle.

Curiously enough, it was not many months later, that he again espied a ship coming toward the island. This time, however, she was not of so distinct a type that he could at once decide whether she was Spanish or French. Desiring a closer examination, he ran eagerly down toward the beach and was proceeding along through the underbrush with insufficient caution, when he suddenly came straight upon several of the crew before he even so much as knew they had landed. On the instant he perceived they were Spanish and made off. The others were struck dumb with astonishment at coming suddenly on so wild appearing a man on what they had believed to be an uninhabited island. However, they recovered themselves at once, fired shots after him and followed hot on his heels. They being close upon him, he suddenly shinned up a tree and hid himself in its branches. The Spaniards pursued him to the very foot of the tree and there losing track of him lingered long on the spot just beneath him. They even looked up frequently into the branches and Selkirk's heart went pounding, for had they perceived him, he could scarcely have got out of range of their firelocks, but so dense were the leaves they did not discover him and at length they retired once more to their camp.

Henceforth, after his disappointment in this second ship, Selkirk seemed even less than ever to set his heart on leaving the island. And indeed after this no other ship again came near.

He dwelt now in a state of great cheerfulness and even joy, not only reconciled to his lot but taking much pleasure in it. For the greater part of the year the sky was cheerful and serene, the air temperate and his little hut was on the edge of a spacious wood abloom with flowers. He kept it always clean and well-ordered and had even come to ornament it with the fragrant green boughs of trees, so that it formed a delicious bower around which played soft and balmy breezes. It grew to seem to him much like home and he came back to it always after an absence with that pleasant warming of the inner man always experienced by one coming home. Moreover, his cats and tame kids became exceedingly dear to his heart. Though he had at first thought of taming them only to meet his own physical needs, he soon found himself grown mightily fond of the little creatures, and as they grew to love him in return, they in some measure satisfied that natural craving for companionship and affection which dwells ever deep in the heart of man. The kids would come leaping to meet him, licking his hands almost like dogs and the cats would rub against his legs and vie with one another to curl up purring in his lap. He would amuse himself often by teaching his pets to dance and do tricks, singing rousing old songs, and himself dancing with them to the music of his own voice. It was a strange and pretty sight, that!—the great man in his rough and shaggy garments, his face softened with joy of the little creatures, dancing and springing about in their midst, as though they were friends all speaking one language, the language of love that is foreign to none of God's creatures.

Selkirk had his garden, too, and indeed by application of his wits conquered all the inconveniences of his solitude. For food he had all he could wish for of variety and profusion right at hand—goat's flesh and milk, turtle, crawfish, fish, turnips, parsnips, radishes, cabbage, watercress, and a variety of small but delicious black plum, the only article of his diet now not easily procurable, for they grew in places hard to come at high up in the mountains, but were sufficiently delicious to repay the effort of gathering them. He perceived, too, that taste is much a matter of habit, for he had grown to relish his food seasoned with

pimento quite as well as when he had it seasoned with salt.

The wood of the pimento he used entirely for firewood and as it burned, it gave off a most delicious fragrance and served him both for warmth and candle, throwing up a splendid blaze that lit all the darkness about. He was by this time intimately familiar with all the little by-paths of his mountain kingdom and could bound from crag to crag and slip down precipices with the utmost confidence.

So as he surveyed all the beauty and comfort about him and recalled the misery of his earlier state on the island, it seemed to him that his own change of heart had indeed made the promise come true —"The wilderness and the solitary place shall be glad for them and the desert shall rejoice and blossom as the rose."

He no longer missed the society of men. The strife and struggle of humankind seemed far away; God seemed very near. He read: "Behold the hour cometh, yea is now come that ye . . . shall leave me alone, and yet I am not alone because the Father is with me." And as he stood beneath the calm and smiling sky, with the beauty of all out-doors about, and the sea stretching endlessly before him, he felt such a sense of nearness to the great Spirit of the universe, as he had never known in all his life before, and his thoughts were full of reverence and simple childlike peace.

For four years and four months he stayed there, and then one day, the thirty-first of January, 1709, it was, he was as usual surveying the water when he descried two vessels approaching. As they drew near, he saw for a certainty they were English. It was then late in the afternoon and he kept his eyes fixed on them until dark, though he scarcely felt any elation of spirit, as he might had they come some time earlier. After nightfall he gathered plenty of pimento wood and made a great fire to signal the vessels that there was some one alive on the island. All night long he tended it, but he spent none of the time in anxious suspense. Indeed, he thought far more of dressing goat's flesh wherewith to entertain the crew on the morrow, wearied as he knew they must be through months of confinement to salt provisions, than of whether or no his exile was at last to be ended.

During the night he fancied he heard from the vessels the sound of cannon, and later it appeared that his fire had occasioned the greatest surprise and alarm on shipboard. It being believed that the island was uninhabited, the English at once concluded there must be French ships at anchor in the harbor. They had earlier sent out their pinnace to reconnoiter the island, and on seeing the blaze, at once fired the quarter deck gun and several muskets to signal her to return. Then they stood all night to their quarters with decks cleared for action in case the French made at them. As they were forced to get wood and water at any price, they did not sail away, but in the morning made into the bay where they expected to see the boats of the enemy. Finding the coast clear, however, and no sign of ships anywhere, one of the vessels let down her yawl about noon and sent it ashore. Selkirk saw the boat leave the vessel and he at once tied a piece of old linen to a pole and waved it to attract their attention. As the yawl drew near, he saw it contained eight men and heard them call to him asking where was a good place to land. He pointed out the same, and, hurrying there ahead of them, stood ready to receive them as they sprang ashore. At the moment of actually meeting with humankind again, he felt a momentary joy and embraced them each in turn. He then learned that the two vessels were the Duke and Duchess under command of Captain Woodes Rogers, and he invited the sailors hospitably to his hut, but its access was so difficult and intricate, that Captain Dover and his men soon gave over trying to make it, one, Mr. Fry, alone accompanying him there. On the beach Selkirk

entertained the sailors in the best manner he could with the goat's flesh he had prepared. As the men were long absent from their boat, the Duke sent out her pinnace to see what had become of her yawl, suspecting that if there were no French ships in the bay, there might at least be a Spanish garrison lurking somewhere about. The sailors from the pinnace discovered nothing worse than the eight men from the yawl feasting on shore with a wild man, and, perceiving on closer examination that the wild man had an expression kindly, serious, and yet cheerful, they concluded him to be none such dangerous creature as they had at first supposed and invited him to return with them on board. Accordingly, he did so, bearing roast goat's flesh for the crew. As he dined with the Captain it was a remarkable fact that he no longer relished food seasoned with salt, but found himself obliged to acquire again what he had believed to be a perfectly natural taste.

After he had recounted his adventures the renowned Captain Dampier who knew him of old and was then on board as pilot, gave him so good a character that he was at once invited to sail with the Duke as mate. In the afternoon the ships cleared and the sails were taken ashore to be mended, while all hands set to work to lay in wood and provisions. Men were sent with a bull dog to capture goats, but to the surprise of everyone, Selkirk outdistanced them all, even the dog, caught the goats with his hands and bore two of them back on his shoulders.

The Duke and Duchess remained at the island till February the twelfth refitting the ships and getting in stores, and then at last the day came when Selkirk must bid farewell to his little home in the glade, to all his beloved pets, and each spot that had grown dear to him. Whether he truly rejoiced or no, when it came to the actual point of leave-taking, who knows? Who knows?

At length there he was again on shipboard and the coast of Juan Fernandez lay behind him, fading fast into mist and dreams.

The Duke took many prizes and was most successful in its ventures against the Spanish tyrants. In several instances Selkirk was entrusted with the command of small parties sent ashore, where the property and person of the inhabitants were at his mercy, and he showed, by his mild and considerate behavior, that the exalted thoughts of his solitude were not of the kind to vanish.

The Duke and Duchess reached London, October 14, 1711, and Selkirk found himself, when the prize was divided, a rich man. He returned at once to Largo and a joyful reunion with his mother, father, and brothers. But ever after he had no love for great companies of men, choosing rather solitude and the company of his own thoughts. Moreover, he often longed for his pets and his peaceful island where he had felt so near to his Creator, nor did the luxuries riches could provide make him one whit happier than when his wants were confined to the simplest necessities and these supplied by his own efforts alone. "I am now worth eight-hundred pounds," he would often say, "but shall never be so happy as when I was not worth a farthing."

SOLITUDE

THERE is a pleasure in the pathless woods,
There is a rapture on the lonely shore,
There is society where none intrudes
By the deep sea, and music in its roar.
—*Lord Byron*

George Rogers Clark and the Conquest of the Northwest*

THEODORE ROOSEVELT

IN 1776, when independence was declared, the United States included only the thirteen original States on the sea-board. With the exception of a few hunters there were no white men west of the Alleghany Mountains, and there was not even an American hunter in the great country out of which we have since made the States of Illinois, Indiana, Ohio, Michigan, and Wisconsin. All this region north of the Ohio River then formed a part of the Province of Quebec. It was a wilderness of forests and prairies, teeming with game, and inhabited by many warlike tribes of Indians.

Here and there through it were dotted quaint little towns of French Creoles, the most important being Detroit, Vincennes on the Wabash, and Kaskaskia and Kahokia on the Illinois. These French villages were ruled by British officers commanding small bodies of regular soldiers or Tory rangers and Creole partizans. The towns were completely in the power of the British government, none of the American States had actual possession of a foot of property in the Northwestern Territory.

The Northwest was acquired in the midst of the Revolution only by armed conquest, and if it had not been so acquired, it would have remained a part of the British Dominion of Canada.

The man to whom this conquest was due was a famous backwoods leader, a mighty hunter, a noted Indian-fighter, George Rogers Clark. He was a very strong man, with light hair and blue eyes. He was of good Virginian family. Early in his youth, he embarked on the adventurous career of a backwoods surveyor, exactly as Washington and so many other young Virginians of

*Taken from *Hero Tales from American History* by the permission of the publishers, The Century Co.

spirit did at that period. He traveled out to Kentucky soon after it was founded by Boone, and lived there for a year, either at the stations or camping by himself in the woods, surveying, hunting, and making war against the Indians like any other settler, but all the time his mind was bent on vaster schemes than were dreamed of by the men around him. He had his spies out in the Northwestern Territory, and became convinced that with a small force of resolute backwoodsmen he could conquer it for the United States. When he went back to Virginia, Governor Patrick Henry entered heartily into Clark's schemes and gave him authority to fit out a force for his purpose.

In 1778, after encountering endless difficulties and delays, he finally raised a hundred and fifty backwoods riflemen. In May they started down the Ohio in flatboats to undertake the allotted task. They drifted and rowed downstream to the Falls of the Ohio, where Clark founded a log-hamlet, which has since become the great city of Louisville. Here he halted for some days and was joined by fifty or sixty volunteers, but a number of the men deserted, and when, after an eclipse of the sun, Clark again pushed off to go down with the current, his force was but about one hundred and sixty riflemen. All, however, were men on whom he could depend—men well used to frontier warfare. They were tall, stalwart backwoodsmen, clad in the hunting-shirt and leggings that formed the national dress of their kind, and armed with the distinctive weapon of the backwoods, the long-barreled, small-bore rifle.

Before reaching the Mississippi the little flotilla landed, and Clark led his men northward against the Illinois towns. In one of them, Kaskaskia, dwelt the British commander of the entire district up to Detroit. The small garrison and the Creole milita taken together outnumbered Clark's force, and they were in close alliance with the Indians roundabout. Clark was anxious to take the town by surprise and avoid bloodshed, as he believed he could win over the Creoles to the American side. Marching

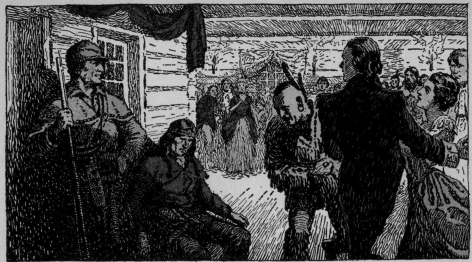

cautiously by night and generally hiding by day, he came to the outskirts of the little village on the evening of July 4, and lay in the woods near by until after nightfall. Fortune favored him. That evening the officers of the garrison had given a great ball to the mirth-loving Creoles, and almost the entire population of the village had gathered in the fort, where the dance was held. While the revelry was at its height, Clark and his backwoodsmen, treading silently through the darkness, came into the town, surprised the sentries, and surrounded the fort without causing any alarm.

All the British and French capable of bearing arms were gathered in the fort to take part in or look on at the merrymaking. When his men were posted Clark walked boldly forward through the open door, and, leaning against the wall, looked at the dancers as they whirled around in the light of the flaring torches. For some moments no one noticed him. Then an Indian who had been lying with his chin on his hand, looking carefully over the gaunt figure of the stranger, sprang to his feet, and uttered the wild war-whoop. Immediately the dancing ceased and the men ran to and fro in confusion, but Clark, stepping forward, bade them be at their ease, but to remember that henceforth they danced under the flag of the United States, and not under that of Great Britain.

The surprise was complete, and no resistance was attempted. For twenty-four hours the Creoles were in abject terror. Then Clark summoned their chief men together and explained that he came as their ally, and not as their foe, and that if they would join with him they should be citizens of the American Republic, and treated in all respects on an equality with their comrades. The Creoles, caring little for the British, and rather fickle of nature, accepted the proposition with joy, and with the most enthusiastic loyalty toward Clark. Not only that, but sending messengers to their kinsmen on the Wabash, they persuaded the people of Vincennes likewise to cast off their allegiance to the British king, and to hoist the American flag.

So far, Clark had conquered with greater ease than he had dared to hope. But when the news reached the British governor, Hamilton, at Detroit, he at once prepared to reconquer the land. He had much greater forces at his command than Clark had, and in the fall of that year he came down to Vincennes by stream and portage, in a great fleet of canoes bearing five hundred fighting men—British regulars, French partisans, and Indians. The Vincennes Creoles refused to fight against the British, and the American officer who had been sent thither by Clark had no alternative but to surrender. If Hamilton had then pushed on and struck Clark in Illinois, having more than treble Clark's force, he could hardly have failed to win the victory, but the season was late and the journey so difficult that he did not believe it could be taken. Accordingly he disbanded the Indians and sent some of his troops back to Detroit, announcing that

when spring came he would march against Clark in Illinois.

If Clark in turn had awaited the blow he would have surely met defeat, but he was a greater man than his antagonist, and he did what the other deemed impossible.

Finding that Hamilton had sent home some of his troops and dispersed all his Indians, Clark realized that his chance was to strike before Hamilton's soldiers assembled again in the spring. Accordingly he gathered together the pick of his men, together with a few Creoles, one hundred and seventy all told, and set out for Vincennes. At first the journey was easy enough, for they passed across the snowy Illinois prairies, broken by great reaches of lofty woods. They killed elk, buffalo, and deer for food, there being no difficulty in getting all they wanted to eat, and at night they built huge fires by which to sleep, and feasted "like Indian war-dancers," as Clark said in his report.

But when, in the middle of February, they reached the drowned lands of the Wabash, where the ice had just broken up and everything was flooded, the difficulties seemed almost insuperable, and the march became painful and laborious to a degree. All day long the troops waded in the icy water, and at night they could with difficulty find some little hillock on which to sleep. Only Clark's indomitable courage and cheerfulness kept the party in heart and enabled them to persevere. However, persevere they did, and at last, on February 23, they came in sight of the town of Vincennes. They captured a Creole who was out shooting ducks, and from him learned that their approach was utterly unsuspected, and that there were many Indians in town.

Clark was now in some doubt as to how to make his fight. The British regulars dwelt in a small fort at one end of the town, where they had two light guns, but Clark feared lest, if he made a sudden night attack, the townspeople and Indians would, from sheer fright, turn against him. He accordingly arranged, just before he himself marched in, to send in the captured duck-hunter, conveying a warning to the Indians and the Creoles that he was about to attack the town, but that his only quarrel was with the British, and that if the other inhabitants would stay in their own homes they would not be molested.

Sending the duck-hunter ahead, Clark took up his march and entered the town just after night-fall. The news conveyed by the released hunter astounded the townspeople, and they talked it over eagerly, and were in doubt what to do. The Indians, not knowing how great might be the force that would assail the town, at once took refuge in the neighboring woods, while the Creoles retired to their own houses. The British knew nothing of what had happened until the Americans had actually entered the streets of the little village. Rushing forward, Clark's men soon penned the regulars within their fort, where they kept them surrounded all night. The next day a party of Indian warriors, who in the British interest had been ravaging the settlements of Kentucky, arrived and entered the town, ignorant that the Americans had captured it. Marching boldly forward to the fort, they suddenly found it beleaguered, and before they could flee they were seized by the backwoodsmen. In their belts they carried the scalps of the slain settlers. The savages were taken redhanded, and the American frontiersmen were in no mood to show mercy. All the Indians were tomahawked in sight of the fort.

For some time the British defended themselves well, but at length their guns were disabled, all of the gunners being picked off by the backwoods marksmen, and finally the garrison dared not so much as appear at a port-hole, so deadly was the fire from the long rifles. Under such circumstances Hamilton was forced to surrender. No attempt was afterward made to molest the Americans in the land they had won, and upon the conclusion of peace the Northwest, which had been conquered by Clark, became part of the United States.

The Rough Rider

A STURDY young fellow, alert and energetic of movement, his spectacles gleaming in the sun, was often to be seen on a tough little western pony riding toward Chimney Butte Ranch on the Little Missouri River, in the Bad Lands of North Dakota. The country around him was wild and desolate, vast stretches of bleak prairie, parched by the scorching sun and varied only by abrupt hills called buttes by the cowboys. It was a land of enormous distances with no farms and no fences, only at wide intervals a little log ranch house with a mud roof. In the fertile river bottoms, long-horned cattle grazed while cowboys dashed recklessly among them on half-broken ponies. Though Theodore Roosevelt had lived all his life in an aristocratic section of New York City, and was a graduate of Harvard, life among the rough plainsmen was what appealed to him most. And so he had bought a ranch and come to live in the West.

At first, when he appeared at a roundup, the cowboys looked at him askance, but he reported to the captain and was assigned to a wagon-boss. Then he deposited his bedding outside the circle of cowboys and ate his supper in silence, turning a deaf ear to gibing remarks about "four eyes" for the cowboys regarded spectacles as the surest sign of a "dude." Day by day he did his job, accepting the discipline of the camp and the orders of the captain. Only when some tough customer made sport of him too boldly, did he reply with his fists and then it was bad for the cowboy!

Read The Boy's Life of Roosevelt *by Hermann Hagedorn; also Roosevelt's* Winning of the West, The Rough Rider, *and* Letters to His Children.

THE TREASURE CHEST

Work on the roundup began at three in the morning, with a yell from the cook, and lasted till sundown or sometimes all night through. In the morning, the cowboys "rode the long circle" in couples driving into the wagon-camp whatever animals were found in the hills. The afternoon was spent in the dangerous work of "cutting out" of the herd the cattle belonging to the various brands. Representatives of each brand rode in succession into the midst of the herd working the animal they were after gently to the edge, and then, with a sudden dash, taking it off at a run.

One evening, a heavy storm broke over the camp. There was a terrific peal of thunder, and the lightning struck almost into the herd. Heads and tails high, off plunged the panic-stricken cattle, and for forty hours Roosevelt was in the saddle driving them together again. After that the cowpunchers decided that the man with the four eyes "had the stuff in him" after all.

Roosevelt lived at Chimney Butte surrounded by bronzed, self-reliant men who were either seasoned plainsmen, like Jim Ferris and the two Merrifields, or keen backwoodsmen from Maine, like Bill Sewall and his nephew, and Will Dow whom Roosevelt had met in his Harvard days when he hunted in the Maine wilderness. No room for social distinctions in such a life. Each man respected the others and all of them worked alike. Roosevelt saddled his own horse, fed the pigs, and now and then washed his own clothes.

In the fall, young Theodore setting out for a roundup in the great cattle country west of the Little Missouri, came with his party to the Big Horn Mountains, where, eight years before, General Custer had been killed by the Indians. Those mountains tempted Roosevelt; so he and Merrifield, with a pack train, left the rest of the party and started up into the mountains along an old Indian trail up the sides of rocky gorges.

They pitched their tents beside a clear mountain brook in a grove of pine trees. From here, they hunted among the peaks round about. The weather was clear and cold with thin ice covering the mountain tarns, and now and again light falls of snow made the forest gleam in the moonlight. Through the frosty air often came the far-off musical note of the bull-elk calling. Roosevelt loved the adventure of the chase, but he loved even more the majesty of the trees and the companionship of all the shy, wild creatures that sprang across his path. When he did set out to hunt, he pursued his aim with dogged persistence. He might be sobbing for breath with sweat streaming into his eyes, but, if he were after a grizzly, after a grizzly he continued to be in spite of all misadventures until he got one. Certainly Theodore Roosevelt never avoided difficulties. He made difficulties contribute to his success.

At length the two men rejoined their party and started on the three-hundred-mile journey home. One night they made their camp beside a dry creek in a broad bottom covered with thick, parched grass. To make sure the campfire should not set the surrounding grass alight, they burned a circle clear, standing about with branches to keep the flames in check. Suddenly, a puff of wind! The fire leapt up and roared like a beast as it raced along the plain. In five minutes the whole bottom would be ablaze. The men fought furiously. Hair and eyebrows were singed black, but they kept on fighting until the flames were subdued.

Winter was hard at Chimney Butte. Trees cracked and groaned from the strain of the frost; even the stars seemed to snap and glitter and, over the frozen river, wolves and lynxes traveled at night. The cattle suffered much and stood in shivering groups huddled in the shelter of the canyons. Every day for Roosevelt began with breakfast at five o'clock, three hours before sunrise; and, from then until dark, he was almost constantly in the saddle, riding among the cattle and turning back any that seemed to be straggling toward the open plain. During the severest weather there were fifty refractory ponies to be broken. Day after day in the cold, Roosevelt labored among them. More than once he was bucked by his steed in the presence of a gallery of grinning cowboys, but, in the end, it was the pony, not Roosevelt, who was broken!

Through the cold, winter evenings, the young man stretched himself out before the great fireplace and often conjured up out of the glowing embers mirth-provoking memories of the queer little boy he had been. Frail in body at first, he had acquired his tough physique only through persistent physical effort; but he had been lively enough when it came to pursuing his hobbies. Oh, that Museum of Natural History he had founded at the age of nine! And the treatise he had written, *Natural History on Insects*, wherein with picturesque spelling, he wrote of "beetlles" and "misqueto hawks," knowledge of whose "habbits" he declared he had gained from his own "ofservation."

Theodore never lost his interest in natural history, but, as he grew to be a youth, there began to awaken in him other and deeper interests. He was thrilled by the heroes of the old epics. He wanted to be like them, like those great doers of deeds who faced both life and death calmly and did not rate life too highly in the balance with what they deemed justice. And gradually, he became more and more deeply aware of the struggle it is to translate dreams into reality. He saw that men accomplish the great purposes of their lives only through endless struggle against the laziness, the love of ease, the doubts and fears of their own hearts.

When he was graduated from college, he decided that the real fighters of his day were the men who went into politics and used their weapons there in behalf of justice and fair play, and so he joined the Twenty-fifth District Republican Association.

Joe Murray, a stockily built Irishman with a strong chin and twinkling eyes, might not be so romantic as an old Norse Viking out of Theodore's epics, but he was a good fighting man when it came to doing battle with the powerful Political Ring and its swaggering "Big Boss," who had governed the Twenty-fifth District in their own interests for many years. Theodore joined forces with Joe Murray, standing vehemently for whatever he deemed was right, and, the first thing he knew, he had defeated the Big Boss and his Ring and was elected a member of the New York State Assembly. There he was distinguishing himself for attacks on many corrupt practices when the death of his young wife, in 1883, sent him West to forget his grief.

Living, working, facing dangers in the West; going out to arrest the desperate leader of a gang' of thieves when it was necessary, Theodore came close to the heart of the "plain American." But the day came at last when he had to return to New York.

Soon it was dishonesty and corruption, instead of thieves, he was fighting as a member of the United States Civil Service Commission and later as Police Commissioner of the City of New York. And when the United States declared war on Spain, because of its tyranny in Cuba, Roosevelt, then Assistant Secretary of the Navy, resigned his post and offered to fight in still another way for what he thought was right by recruiting a regiment of mounted riflemen from among the skilled horsemen of the plains. Of this organization, the Rough Riders, Roosevelt became the Colonel when his superior, Leonard Wood, was advanced in command. So it happened that, at the decisive battle of San Juan Hill, it was Roosevelt with a blue bandana handkerchief with white polka dots floating like a banner from his soiled campaign hat, whom the Rough

AN IMPREGNABLE SHIELD
(From the Pittsburgh *Gazette-Times*)

"NEXT"
(From the Cleveland *Plain Dealer*)

Riders followed to victory in the face of a withering storm of Spanish shrapnel over crest after crest of the San Juan Hills.

Overnight, Roosevelt became a popular hero. He returned to be elected Governor of New York; and, two years later at the National Republican Convention, a perfect stampede of western delegates forced him against his will to accept the nomination for Vice-President with William McKinley as President. Just six months later McKinley was shot by an anarchist, and Roosevelt was summoned to take his place as President of the United States.

Now, for a time, he pursued no more buffalo and elk, but, with the same dogged courage and persistence shown on the western plains, he pursued the Railroad Trust, the Beef Trust, and all other big corporations defrauding the public. He settled a coal strike threatening the welfare of the country; he brought about peace between Russia and Japan, in the days of the Russo-Japanese war. He put through the Panama Canal, and, gradually, he began to stand out as the greatest and most typical American of his day, one who stood vigorously, aggressively if need be, for what he believed to be right using every ounce of energy and enthusiasm that was in him to translate ideals into accomplished facts.

Princess Nelly and the Seneca Chief*

IN THE days of the American Revolution, western Pennsylvania was inhabited by different tribes of Indians. The Delawares were friends of the United States, but the Iroquois were friends and allies of England. Very few white settlers had ventured into those parts, for the life of frontiersmen, amid such roving bands of red men, was one of constant peril. Only in the vicinity of the military garrison at Pittsburgh, or Fort Pitt as it was then called, was there any sense of security. Here on the banks of the Plum River, there settled one Mr. Lytle from Baltimore, with his wife and children. For some time they lived in uneventful comfort, experiencing no hostile visits from the Indians.

One morning in the autumn of 1779, however, Mr. Lytle set out with his men to help a neighbor at some distance raise a new building on his farm, leaving his wife and children without a man to protect them. After the noonday meal Maggie and Tom, the two younger children, went to romp in the garden. Nelly, a child of nine, and her brother, two years younger, were at play in a wooded hollow just behind their father's house.

It was an afternoon of glowing splendor; the meadows swam in golden haze, the hillsides were purple with shadows, and the river swept its shining path through banks of flaming color. Over all seemed to lie a wondrous, golden peace. Behind the children, in the cabin, their mother sang at her work. No scene could have appeared more homelike and serene. But, suddenly, Nelly stopped playing and clutched her brother by the shoulder.

"Look," she whispered, "behind that log!"

The boy peered off in the direction which his sister had indicated. Behind the log, what was it moving—a gaily-colored bird or feathers on the head of an Indian?

The boy answered not a word. Seizing his sister by the hand, he dragged her off toward the house. The children were accus-

*This is a true story of the little girl who later became Mrs. John Kinzie, one of the earliest settlers of Chicago.

tomed to friendly Delawares, but these came honestly straight to the house; they never came lurking, hiding. Breathless, the two burst into the cabin. "Mother," they cried, "there's an Indian down in the hollow hiding behind the trees."

The mother looked up from her knitting, half-smiling, half-annoyed. "What, only one?" she said. "Usually you fancy a score! The neighbors' children have frightened you with their ridiculous stories. Our farm is too near Fort Pitt for the Indians to dare give us trouble. When will you stop mistaking every whisk of a squirrel's tail among the leaves for a band of Indians? Go back to your play and put aside childish fears."

Nelly and her brother hung their heads, humbled by the rebuke. True, they had more than once come running with false alarms, yet this time they felt so sure of what they had seen! They went with lagging steps back to the little hollow. A different place it seemed now from what it had been a few moments before. The golden peace had fled, a lurid loneliness brooded about, the shadows had grown fantastic. Nelly and her brother had no wish to play. They seated themselves on a log and held close to each other.

"Hark!" whispered Nelly. "There's a rustling in the bushes."

Just then, "Bob-white!" a quail whistled somewhere near. Immediately, "Bob-white!" a second note answered the first.

"It's never birds that are calling like that!" said the boy.

The children were gazing so intently in the direction of the log behind which they had seen the feathers, that everything else sank out of their sight. Suddenly, big red hands were clapped over their mouths from behind. Two great Indians seized them and carried them into the forest. Behind, still faintly sounded, as if from another world, the voice of their mother singing and the laughter of Maggie and Tom.

At some distance from the house, the Indians set the children down and compelled them to walk by themselves, making threatening gestures to force them to keep silence. Then they hurried them off through the forest and soon joined a band of their fellows, all so fierce and splendidly dressed that the children knew they were not Delawares from the neighborhood.

For some little distance, they dragged and drove the children along in silence. The little boy whimpered once, but then he squared his shoulders, sniffed back his tears, flung back his head, and marched sturdily on. As to Nelly, now that the worst had come, her spirit rose boldly to meet it. She took her brother's hand with a motherly air of protection and walked staunchly by his side, her eyes flashing lightning if one of the Indians but showed signs of molesting the boy.

Through the leafy aisles of the forest, on and on they marched. When it began to grow dusk the Indians halted, made their camp for the night, lit their campfire, and set men on watch. Then the children were left to themselves. Nelly took her brother in her arms and the two wept quietly together.

Suddenly there stood before them a tall and majestic Indian of a strong and forceful countenance, yet strangely mild and gentle. With Indian words, he tried to soothe them and pulling up armfuls of grass, he made them a bed. Then he shared with them his own stock of dried meat and parched corn and gave them to understand by signs that no further evil would befall them.

Scarcely had he thus settled them, somewhat calmed and comforted on the bed he had prepared, when, in the glare of the campfire, a second party of Indians belonging to the same band appeared. With them, they brought a white prisoner. Her pale face, lit by the flames, stood out quite distinctly in the blaze against the black of the forest. Then the children saw that the prisoner was their mother.

With little shrieks of relief, they ran and clung to her skirts while she covered them with kisses. The Indians made no attempt to separate the three, but allowed the mother to go off with the children to their bed. There, as they sat by themselves, Mrs.

THE TREASURE CHEST

Lytle told the children how the Indians had fallen upon her while she was at work and borne her off a prisoner.

"And Maggie and Tom, where are they?" sobbed Nelly.

The mother bowed her head. "I do not know," she whispered.

From the peculiar manner in which these Indians painted their bodies, Mrs. Lytle guessed they were Senecas, one of the Iroquois tribes, and she devoutly hoped their purpose was to hold the prisoners for ransom.

Early the next morning, they started once more on their march. It then appeared that the Indian who had shared his supper with the children was none other than the chief, Corn-Planter, himself. Day after day they marched, but the prisoners were not ill-treated, and Corn-Planter took a wonderful fancy to Nelly. He took her up to ride before him on his horse, offered her some little trinket, or shared his food with her and, at nightfall, he never failed to see that a couch of soft grass was made ready for her. On his partiality for Nelly, Mrs. Lytle built bright hopes that he would keep them all safely and yield them up soon for ransom.

At length the party reached the picturesque little village of the Senecas, nestling 'mid fragrant pines, near the headwaters of the Allegheny. Corn-Planter took his prisoners to the principal lodge of the village where his mother lived, a dignified, stately old woman who was called the Old Queen.

"Take these white people," Corn-Planter said, "and treat them kindly. Many horses and guns will be given to buy them back."

But as soon as Mrs. Lytle and her children had left the lodge,

he said to the Old Queen: "My mother, I bring you this little white girl to take the place of the brother who was killed by the Lenape six moons ago. She shall be to you a daughter, to me a sister. She shall dwell in our lodge forever. The boy and his mother may be bought for a ransom, but little sister shall be ours."

So the Old Queen took Nelly to her heart in place of the little boy she had lost and showed her every sign of affection that an Indian can display. Moreover, as her son had commanded, she provided for the prisoners every comfort the village afforded.

Meantime, late in the evening of the day when Mrs. Lytle and the children had been captured, the father came whistling home. No lights in the windows of the house! Within, no fire on the hearth, no kettle simmering above with grateful aroma of the evening meal, not a single human being anywhere about! Only the mother's knitting hastily dropped in a chair and a dilapidated rag doll deserted in a corner! Alarmed beyond measure, the father hastened off to his nearest neighbor, who lived at a considerable distance. The man had no tidings to give him, but all the men in his household joined the search for the missing ones.

At length, in the house of another neighbor, Mr. Lytle found Lizzie, their servant-maid. With many tears, she told how the Indians had descended on the house. At the first alarm, she said, she had run to an outer kitchen to hide under a brewing tub. There she had remained until the Indians departed, when she fled to this neighbor's house.

The father and his neighbors searched the whole night long, but still found no trace of the family. Toward morning, Mr. Lytle recalled that there was an old settler who lived alone far up the valley. To his cabin the searchers went and this man told them that as he was working in his field at sunset, he had seen some strange Indians passing at a distance from him. As they wound along the brow of the hill, their forms clearly silhouetted against the sunset sky, he could see that they had with them a white woman as a prisoner. Here, the miserable father felt sure was news of his wife and he determined to go to Fort Pitt to ask assistance of the Commandant and Indian Agent there.

Accordingly, he and his party proceeded down the valley just as the sun was rising. On their way, they came suddenly upon a hut which they had searched the night before and found apparently deserted.

To their surprise, they now saw standing on the high bank before it a little boy and girl holding fast to each others' hands. Mr. Lytle at once recognized his two youngest children, Maggie and Tom; and, in another moment, they were fast in their father's arms and pouring out their tale in his ears.

"We were in the garden, father," cried the boy, "and then the Indians came, so many Indians, into the yard by the house!"

"An' 'en," sobbed the little girl, "Tommy, he pulled me over the fence, an' we hided ourselves in the bushes and runned an' runned so far! An' where's my mother? I want my mother!"

It appeared that the boy who was only six years of age, had shown the most remarkable courage, devotion, and intelligence in saving himself and his sister from the redmen. He had, on the first alarm, half-pulled and half-pushed the little girl over the garden fence and into a neighboring field overrun with blackberry bushes and wild raspberry. Here they hid themselves, having the sense and self-command to make no outcry at all until all was quiet and no Indians were in sight, when they attempted to force a way through the field in a direction opposite to the house.

Unfortunately, the little girl, in her play in the garden, had pulled off her shoes and stockings and the ground being very rough, uneven, and covered with briers, she soon found her feet so cut and bruised, that she sank to the ground and declared she could not go a single step further. Then the boy took off his own stockings, put them on her feet, and gave her his shoes also, himself going barefoot over the torturing ground.

The little creature tried to scuffle along in the shoes so many sizes too large, but they kept slipping off altogether so she could not possibly wear them. Then the boy took back the shoes, but he stuck faithfully to his sister, patiently lifting her over the roughest spots and, part of the time, half-carrying her.

Thus they made their way out of the field and into an unenclosed pasture. Here, to their great delight, they saw some cows peacefully feeding. These cows, as they knew, belonged to old Granny Myers. But in what direction her cottage lay, they had not the slightest idea. With a wisdom that might have done credit to a man, the little boy said to his sister, "Let's hide until sunset. Then the cows will go home, and we can follow them."

This was what the children did, but, when they reached Granny Myers' hut in the wake of the lowing cattle, they found the house locked and deserted. Tired and hungry, they could go no further. So they managed, with much effort, to get a few drops of milk from the cows, then they lay down to sleep beneath a discarded bedstead that stood behind the house. When their father and his party had approached the place during the night, they had mistaken the shouts of the searchers for the whooping of Indians, and, far from revealing themselves, had kept well out of sight.

Mr. Lytle now placed his two youngest children in security at Fort Pitt, where he received from the Commandant a detachment of soldiers to aid in the search for the rest of his family. Circumstances soon pointed to the Senecas as the probable marauders, and the relief party at once directed their search among the villages of that tribe. It was necessary, however, to proceed with the greatest caution, for the Iroquois, being allies of Great Britain, were decidedly hostile to the Americans. Thus a long time passed before the father at last reached Corn-Planter's village.

What was his unspeakable joy to find here his wife and the two older children. At once he began to enter into negotiations with Corn-Planter for ransoming his family. Mrs. Lytle and the boy? Yes, Corn-Planter readily agreed on a price for them and set them free at once, but Nelly? No, never! She was the adopted child of the tribe, she was his sister! She was dear to him and he would not part with her! To every entreaty of the parents, even of Nelly herself, to every increase of the price offered for the child, Corn-Planter only grunted, "Ugh! Ugh!" and shook his head with decision.

Finding every effort useless, the father was compelled to take his sorrowful departure, and set out once more for home with such of his loved ones as he had been fortunate enough to recover. Little Nelly threw herself into the arms of her father and mother almost in despair as they bade each other farewell. The hearts of all were heavy with grief, but, there was nothing else to be done. So Mr. and Mrs. Lytle set out for home with their son, trusting that, at some future time, they might recover their daughter.

Never for a moment did Mr. Lytle relax his efforts in Nelly's behalf. He made a long and dangerous journey to the Canadian frontier, hoping to gain the assistance of the British Indian Agent, a man named Colonel Johnson. Seeing in the stricken father, no American enemy, but a human being in need, Colonel Johnson promised to do everything in his power to get Nelly from the Indians. As soon as spring had come, he went in person to Corn-Planter's village and made him a splendid offer of many guns and horses if he would release the child. But Corn-Planter answered the British Agent as he had answered the Americans with nothing more than two grunts and a most decisive shake of his head.

Thus the months lengthened into years, while Nelly dwelt like a princess in the lodge of the Old Queen, the beloved of all the tribe. The principal seat in the lodge was always reserved for her, the most delicate food, the handsomest silver brooches and strings of wampum were for her; no efforts were spared to make her happy.

For a long time Nelly resisted any attempts at consolation, crying continually for her mother, but she was by nature affectionate, and the unbounded tenderness of those among whom she now dwelt called forth a response in her heart. Though she could never cease longing for her own mother, she grew to regard Corn-Planter and the Old Queen with reverence and love. She learned to speak their language and even found much joy in sharing the bustling life of the village. Wherever she went, whether gathering wild rice from the river in her little birch-bark canoe, hoeing corn in the cornfield, or playing at ball or bowl, she displayed such unbounded energy, that the Indians gave her the name of "The Ship-under-Full-Sail" and by that picturesque name, they called her.

Thus four years passed by. Then in 1783, came peace between the United States and Great Britain. The Revolution was ended. In consequence, a general pacification of the Indian tribes took place and fresh hopes of recovering their daughter arose in the hearts of Mr. and Mrs. Lytle. They removed to Fort Niagara near which was the Great Council Fire of the Senecas, whither, once every year, came the sachems and chiefs from the various villages to decide the affairs of their nation. The kindly Colonel Johnson readily undertook fresh negotiations with Corn-Planter and again proceeded in person to the village at Olean Point.

His visit occurred at the most propitious of seasons, for the Indians were celebrating the Festival of the Corn when he arrived among them. It was the one season of the year most remarkable for general joy. Gaily was the village decked with golden ears of corn and glowing autumn leaves. Young men and dusky maidens stripped the husks from the ears. Here some played games of ball, tossing little balls of deerskin; there gaily-painted warriors gathered in a dance, while beneath the fragrant pine trees old men squatted, smoking, and now and then grunting approval.

Colonel Johnson was received with all due consideration, and, when he spoke of Nelly, she was summoned in to meet him, dressed in a petticoat of blue broadcloth bordered with gay-colored ribbons. Around her neck were strings of purple wampum. Her hair was loaded with beads, her leggins were of scarlet cloth, and her moccasins of deerskin were embroidered with porcupine quills. All the love that had been showered on the child was evidenced in her garments. Nevertheless, Colonel Johnson ventured to tell Corn-Planter how the mother and father of his little sister had given up their home and friends and come hundreds of miles to settle in a strange land on the bare hope of sometimes looking on their loved one. Then at last the heart of the chief was softened. There was soon to be held at Fort Niagara, on the British side of the river, the Grand Council of the Senecas, and thither Corn-Planter promised to come, bringing his sister with him that her parents might have just a glimpse of her. But he exacted a solemn promise that no effort should be made to reclaim the child.

Accordingly, in due time, Chief Corn-Planter set out with Nelly on horseback beside him, her heart beating fast with joy at thought of seeing her mother. She had promised the Chief never to leave him without his permission, and he had perfect faith in her word.

Meantime, as the chiefs and warriors arrived in successive bands at the fort, the anxious parents watched longingly for a first sight of their daughter. At length, a group of Indians was discerned emerging from the forest on the American side of the river, and Mr. and Mrs. Lytle could see that Nelly was with them.

The commanding officer sent boats across to fetch Corn-Planter and his party, but the Chief entered one of these alone with his

little sister. He held her close by the hand until the boat touched the bank, then the young girl rushed forward into her mother's arms and the two began hugging and kissing as though they had been famished with longing for each other.

When he beheld that sight, the great chief could withstand no longer. He spoke no word, but made an eloquent gesture of surrender. Then he turned and ordered the oarsmen to row him back alone to the farther bank. All the way over the river, he stood in the stern of the boat, looking back with folded arms for a farewell glimpse of his loved one—majestic, almost heroic, a noble statue in bronze, savage though he was, of sublime renunciation. No arguments nor entreaties could induce him to remain at the Council. Having gained the opposite side of the river, he called his braves about him and made off into the forest.

And so it came about that little Nelly saw her good friend, the Chief, no more, but she never forgot him. Through all her life there remained in her heart a tender memory of the strong and forceful warrior, who had been to her as gentle as a woman.

Hiawatha's Fasting*

A Legend of the First Indian Corn

HENRY WADSWORTH LONGFELLOW

You shall hear how Hi-a-wa'tha
Prayed and fasted in the forest,
Not for greater skill in hunting,
Not for greater craft in fishing,
Not for triumphs in the battle,
And renown among the warriors,
But for profit of the people,
For advantage of the nations.

First he built a lodge for fasting,
Built a wigwam in the forest,
By the shining Big-Sea-Water.
In the blithe and pleasant Spring-time,
In the Moon of Leaves he built it,
And, with dreams and visions many,
Seven whole days and nights he fasted.

On the first day of his fasting
Through the leafy woods he wandered;
Saw the deer start from the thicket,
Saw the rabbit in his burrow,
Heard the pheasant, Be'na, drumming,
Heard the squirrel, Ad-ji-dau'mo,
Rattling in his hoard of acorns,
Saw the pigeon, the O-me'me,
Building nests among the pine-trees,
And in flocks the wild goose, Wa'wa,
Flying to the fen-lands northward,
Whirring, wailing far above him.
"Master of Life!" he cried, desponding,
"Must our lives depend on these things?"

*Used by permission of, and by special arrangement with, Houghton Mifflin Company, the publishers.

On the next day of his fasting
By the river's brink he wandered,
Through the Musk'o-day, the meadow,
Saw the wild rice, Mah-no-mo'nee,
Saw the blueberry, Mee-nah'ga,
And the strawberry, O-dah'min,
And the grape-vine, the Be-mah'gut,
Trailing o'er the alder-branches,
Filling all the air with fragrance!
"Master of Life!" he cried, desponding,
"Must our lives depend on these things?"
    On the third day of his fasting
By the lake he sat and pondered,
By the still, transparent water;
Saw the sturgeon, Nah'ma, leaping,
Scattering drops like beads of wampum,
Saw the yellow perch, the Sah'wa,
Like a sunbeam in the water,
Saw the pike, the Mask-e-no'zha,
And the Shaw'-ga-shee', the craw-fish!
"Master of Life!" he cried, desponding,
"Must our lives depend on these things?"
    On the fourth day of his fasting
In his lodge he lay exhausted;
From his couch of leaves and branches
Gazing with half-open eyelids,
Full of shadowy dreams and visions,
On the dizzy, swimming landscape,
On the gleaming of the water,
On the splendor of the sunset.
    And he saw a youth approaching,
Dressed in garments green and yellow,

THE TREASURE CHEST

Coming through the purple twilight,
Through the splendor of the sunset;
Plumes of green bent o'er his forehead,
And his hair was soft and golden.

Standing at the open doorway,
Long he looked at Hiawatha,
Looked with pity and compassion
On his wasted form and features,
And, in accents like the sighing
Of the South-Wind in the tree-tops,
Said he, "O my Hiawatha!
All your prayers are heard in heaven,
For you pray not like the others;
Not for greater skill in hunting,
Not for greater craft in fishing,
Not for triumph in the battle,
Nor renown among the warriors,
But for profit of the people,
For advantage of the nations.

"From the Master of Life descending,
I, the friend of man, Mon-da'min,
Come to warn you and instruct you,
How by struggle and by labor
You shall gain what you have prayed for.
Rise up from your bed of branches,
Rise, O youth, and wrestle with me!"

Faint with famine, Hiawatha
Started from his bed of branches,
From the twilight of his wigwam
Forth into the flush of sunset
Came, and wrestled with Mon-da'min;
At his touch he felt new courage,

Felt new life and hope and vigor
Run through every nerve and fibre.
　So they wrestled there together
In the glory of the sunset,
And the more they strove and struggled,
Stronger still grew Hiawatha;
Till the darkness fell around them,
And the heron, the Shuh-shuh'gah,
From her nest among the pine-trees,
Gave a cry of lamentation,
Gave a scream of pain and famine.
　" 'Tis enough!" then said Monda'min,
Smiling upon Hiawatha,
"But to-morrow, when the sun sets,
I will come again to try you."
And he vanished, and was seen not;
Whether sinking as the rain sinks,
Whether rising as the mists rise,
Hiawatha saw not, knew not,
Only saw that he had vanished,
Leaving him alone and fainting,
With the misty lake below him,
And the reeling stars above him.
　On the morrow and the next day,
When the sun through heaven descending,
Like a red and burning cinder
From the heart of the Great Spirit,
Fell into the western waters,
Came Monda'min for the trial,
For the strife with Hiawatha;
Came as silent as the dew comes,
From the empty air appearing,

The Negro-English composer, Samuel Coleridge-Taylor, has written
a cantata, *Hiawatha's Wedding Feast*, a setting of Longfellow's poem.

THE TREASURE CHEST

Into empty air returning,
Taking shape when earth it touches,
But invisible to all men
In its coming and its going.

Thrice they wrestled there together
In the glory of the sunset,
Till the darkness fell around them,
Till the heron, the Shuh-shuh'gah,
From her nest among the pine-trees,
Uttered her loud cry of famine,
And Monda'min paused to listen.

Tall and beautiful he stood there,
In his garments green and yellow;
To and fro his plumes above him
Waved and nodded with his breathing,
And the sweat of the encounter
Stood like drops of dew upon him.

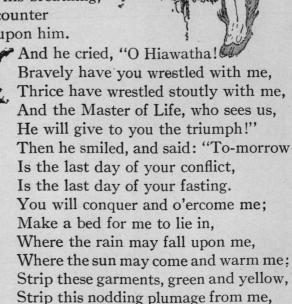

And he cried, "O Hiawatha!
Bravely have you wrestled with me,
Thrice have wrestled stoutly with me,
And the Master of Life, who sees us,
He will give to you the triumph!"
Then he smiled, and said: "To-morrow
Is the last day of your conflict,
Is the last day of your fasting.
You will conquer and o'ercome me;
Make a bed for me to lie in,
Where the rain may fall upon me,
Where the sun may come and warm me;
Strip these garments, green and yellow,
Strip this nodding plumage from me,
Lay me in the earth, and make it

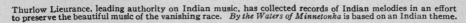

Thurlow Lieurance, leading authority on Indian music, has collected records of Indian melodies in an effort to preserve the beautiful music of the vanishing race. *By the Waters of Minnetonka* is based on an Indian theme.

Soft and loose and light above me.
"Let no hand disturb my slumber,
Let no weed nor worm molest me,
Let not Kah-gah-gee', the raven,
Come to haunt me and molest me,
Only come yourself to watch me,
Till I wake, and start, and quicken,
Till I leap into the sunshine."
And thus saying, he departed;
Peacefully slept Hiawatha,
But he heard the Wa-wo-nais'sa,
Heard the whip-poor-will complaining,
Perched upon his lonely wigwam;
Heard the rushing Se-bo-wish'a,
Heard the rivulet rippling near him,
Talking to the darksome forest;
Heard the sighing of the branches,
As they lifted and subsided
At the passing of the night-wind,
Heard them, as one hears in slumber
Far-off murmurs, dreamy whispers;
Peacefully slept Hiawatha.
On the morrow came No-ko'mis,
On the seventh day of his fasting,
Came with food for Hiawatha,
Came imploring and bewailing,
Lest his hunger should o'ercome him,
Lest his fasting should be fatal.
But he tasted not, and touched not.
Only said to her, "No-ko'mis,
Wait until the sun is setting,
Till the darkness falls around us,

THE TREASURE CHEST

Till the heron, the Shuh-shuh'gah,
Crying from the desolate marshes,
Tells us that the day is ended."
  Homeward weeping went No-ko'mis,
Sorrowing for her Hiawatha,
Fearing lest his strength should fail him,
Lest his fasting should be fatal.
He meanwhile sat weary waiting
For the coming of Monda'min,
Till the shadows, pointing eastward,
Lengthened over field and forest,
Till the sun dropped from the heaven,
As a red leaf in the Autumn
Falls and floats upon the water,
Falls and sinks into its bosom.
  And behold! the young Monda'min,
With his soft and shining tresses,
With his garments green and yellow,
With his long and glossy plumage,
Stood and beckoned at the doorway.
And as one in slumber walking,
Pale and haggard, but undaunted,
From the wigwam Hiawatha
Came and wrestled with Monda'min.
  Round about him spun the landscape,
Sky and forest reeled together,
And his strong heart leaped within him,
As the sturgeon leaps and struggles
In a net to break its meshes.
Like a ring of fire around him
Blazed and flared the red horizon,
And a hundred suns seemed looking

At the combat of the wrestlers.
    Suddenly upon the greensward
All alone stood Hiawatha,
Panting with his wild exertion,
Palpitating with the struggle;
And before him, breathless, lifeless,
Lay the youth, with hair dishevelled,
Plumage torn, and garments tattered;
Dead he lay there in the sunset.
    And victorious Hiawatha
Made the grave as he commanded,
Stripped the garments from Monda'min,
Stripped his tattered plumage from him,
Laid him in the earth, and made it
Soft and loose and light above him;
And the heron, the Shuh-shuh'gah,
From the melancholy moorlands,
Gave a cry of lamentation,
Gave a cry of pain and anguish.
    Homeward then went Hiawatha
To the lodge of old Noko'mis
And the seven days of fasting
Were accomplished and completed.
But the place was not forgotten
Where he wrestled with Monda'min;
Nor forgotten nor neglected
Was the grave where lay Monda'min,
Sleeping in the rain and sunshine;
Where his scattered plumes and garments
Faded in the rain and sunshine.
    Day by day did Hiawatha
Go to wait and watch beside it;

THE TREASURE CHEST

Kept the dark mould soft above it,
Kept it clean from weeds and insects,
Drove away, with scoffs and shoutings,
Kah-gah-gee', the king of ravens.
  Till at length a small green feather
From the earth shot slowly upward,
Then another and another,
And before the Summer ended
Stood the maize in all its beauty,
With its shining robes about it,
And its long, soft, yellow tresses;
And in rapture Hiawatha
Cried aloud, "It is Monda'min!
Yes, the friend of man, Monda'min!"
  Then he called to old Noko'mis
And I-a'goo, the great boaster,
Showed them where the maize was growing,
Told them of his wondrous vision,
Of his wrestling and his triumph,
Of this new gift to the nations,
Which should be their food forever.
  And still later, when the Autumn
Changed the long, green leaves to yellow,
And the soft and juicy kernels
Grew like wampum hard and yellow,
Then the ripened ears he gathered,
Stripped the withered husks from off them,
As he once had stripped the wrestler,
Gave the first Feast of Monda'min,
And made known unto the people
This new gift of the Great Spirit.

Peer Gynt*

Told from the Play by Henrik Ibsen

LITTLE, old, withered Ase had a harum-scarum son. A charming rascal, yes! But a ne'er-do-well if there ever was one. Ase was a poor widow. Her husband had dissipated all their worldly goods and she had need of a sturdy, industrious son to help her. But that son of hers, Peer Gynt—lazy, idle, a dreamer! What tales the fellow could tell! He could wind his mother around his little finger with his yarns and his romancing. Maybe she scolded him roundly when he got into a brawl or idled his time away, but, let some one else try to scold him—they had to reckon with Ase!

One day Peer went out hunting, and Ase hoped that at least he would bring home some game to eat. She stood in front of her farmhouse watching for him to come home. At last there he came, the idler, leaping from crag to crag, his clothes in tatters as usual, and without e'er a sign of game.

"Ne'er-do-well!" shrieked Ase. "When the work is worst, you rush off to hunt in the mountains and come home in rags and tatters, bringing no game to eat. But, with round and innocent eyes, you want me to believe the lies you tell in excuse."

"Ah, but mother," cried Peer, taking her in his arms and giving her a loud smack. "You should just have seen the reindeer I shot by the deep mountain lake where the ice floes crash on the shore and glaciers lie all around. Bang went my gun and he dropped! Down dropped the buck in the snow. In a moment, I leaped on his back with his left ear fast in my grasp. But, then, what think you he did? He jumped up with me on his back. On the very edge of the lake, he cut a path through the sky. Swerving around and shying, he tried to scale the heavens. Then down he plunged in the lake! Down, down, down we went! All about us the foam flecks dashed. We plunged through the water splashing."

*The *Peer Gynt Suite*, written for a performance of Ibsen's play by the greatest Norwegian composer, Grieg (1843–1907), gives the mood of different incidents in this drama. It is often found on musical programs for children.

THE TREASURE CHEST

"Oh, my son!" cried Ase, knowing well that the boy was lying even while her mother love was smitten with care for his safety. "You did not hurt yourself in this awful ride on a reindeer?"

"No," Peer answered her easily. "The buck swam and I clung fast. At last we reached the northern shore. I leaped from the reindeer in safety and came running home to thee."

"The Lord be thanked," cried Ase, "that you have not broken your back!" For a moment she stood open-mouthed then, suddenly recovering from the spell of his marvelous lying, she burst out in a rage: "Holy Cross, what lies you tell! See that poor farmhouse of ours, windows broken and stuffed with cloths, hedges flat and gates a-rattle with naught to keep cattle from straying. What have we now of the glory left us by your good grandsire?"

"Oh," Peer shrugged his shoulders and answered her very airily, "where are the snows of yesteryear?"

"Peer, you are strong of arm," the mother urged in distress. "You should be my prop and stay, managing field and farm, yet you lounge around like a drone, lazy before the fireside. You go to feasts with the young folks or fight with any bold rascal. In everything you do, you forever shame and mock me!"

"Let me be," cried Peer. "No one knows how fortune changes. I will be a king or an emperor. Give me time and you shall see!"

"While you hunted the reindeer," Ase answered bitterly, "Mads Moen won Ingrid, the heiress, who has ever favored you. Their wedding will be tomorrow. Guests are already gathering."

"Very well," laughed Peer. "We'll go to the wedding, too."

"You, in rags and tatters like that!" Ase shrieked in her anger.

"Certainly, just like this Peer will go to the wedding, and you will go along, too!" He lifted her in his arms and plunged into the river to wade to the other side.

"You beast, put me down!" cried Ase, pulling his hair in rage. But Peer only laughed and said, "We'll play at Peer and the reindeer. I'm the reindeer and you are Peer."

"Don't drop me," cried Ase in terror when they reached the middle of the river.

"Won't you give the reindeer a kiss for bearing you over the water?" Peer airily waded ashore.

Ase swiftly boxed his ears. "Put me down!" she cried, kicking with rage. "I'll walk to the wedding and tell all the guests what kind of a lad you are."

"Then I must go alone." Peer lifted her high in his arms and set her down on the roof of a millhouse near the river.

"Let me down," screamed Ase.

"Gladly, if you'll consent not to tell tales on me."

Ase plucked a sod of grass from the growth in the mud on the rooftop and threw it at the young rascal. "Reindeer-rider! Liar! Brute!" she choked in her anger.

"Goodbye," laughed Peer gaily, "and, remember, you'd better keep still or you'll tumble off the roof."

He strode away and left her to get out of her plight as she could.

Yes, he would go to the wedding. But, as he went on up the path, he suddenly stopped to rest lying flat on the purple heather and gazing up at the sky. Straightway the clouds set him dream-

"Morning Mood," the first movement of Grieg's *Peer Gynt Suite*, pictures the sun dawning slowly on the world till it bursts forth in all its glory. So Peer's dreams dawn and glow into glorious pictures of himself, as king.

ing. Some day great crowds of people would hail him as their emperor! He would wear a long, costly coat and ride on a splendid horse, its harness all glittering with gold. And people would shout, "This is Peer! None is like him under the sun!"

How he did love to dream! Life was dull and gray on the little farm left by his father. Who wished to work and toil? Escaping life in such daydreams—that was his mode of living. Ase could day-dream, too, but Ase, out of her love, dreamed how her son should be happy. Peer dreamed of himself, always of just Peer Gynt.

Wedding guests, passing by, aroused Peer from his romancing. He rose and went on his way. At the farm of Ingrid's father, all was merrymaking with dancing on the green in the center of the trim farm buildings. A fiddler sat on a table; cook-maids went to and fro; the poor little weakling bridegroom, whom Ingrid was to marry, fluttered from guest to guest; and elderly people sat cozily talking here and there.

Impudently and boldly Peer tried to joke with the girls and hint he would like to dance. One after another they snubbed him. He thought too well of himself. He was a windbag for boasting. He was an idler, a brawler. They gave him back saucy words. At last Peer's impudence failed him. He slunk away by the fence.

Then, all at once, there came into the busy farmplace, a shy and lovely young maiden with hair that swam like gold. She was not gay and bold like the other mischievous farm girls, but modest and sweet of demeanor. Holding a prayer book in one hand and her little sister by the other, she followed her mother and father.

Suddenly Peer was struck straight to the core of his heart with a feeling honest and real, such as in all his life he had never known before. "Saw you ever so sweet a maid?" he asked of a lad standing by. "Is she a stranger in these parts?"

"Yes," replied the lad, "her people came recently to our neigh-borhood. Solveig is the maid's name; her little sister is Helga."

His impudence gone for the moment, Peer went to the father.

"May I dance with your daughter?" he asked.

"Aye," the father answered, "when we have greeted our hostess."

Solveig's shy glance rested sweetly on Peer for a moment as she went on into the house. But, while she was gone, some rough lads came up to Peer with brandy. They all began to drink and to cry out noisily: "Peer, tell us one of your seven great stories."

"One day I caught the Devil," Peer was the big man again. "I shut him up in a nut. You should have heard him inside. He rumbled and grumbled and bumbled like a raging bumblebee."

"Tell us one better still!" The lads set Peer off again on his biggest, most boastful stories; but, while he was drinking and boasting, Solveig came out of the house. Peer's eyes lit with delight.

"Solveig!" he cried. "How good! You have come again, my dear! Now I shall whirl you gaily." But, as he took her hand, she looked at him with sweet, clear eyes that seemed to see straight into him.

"You've been drinking," she said. "Let me go! I will not dance!"

"You think I look like a tramp," Peer now began to storm. "You're ashamed to be seen with me."

"You're not like a tramp at all." Her eyes appeared still to see right through the drunken, boastful, selfish outside of Peer to something real and fine that was hidden deep down within him. "You're not like a tramp at all. But still I will not dance!"

"Then I'll change myself into a troll." Peer's voice grew terrifying. "I'll eat you and your little sister. Aye, I'll eat you both!" But, as suddenly as he had grown so overbearing and frightful, he changed to tender pleading. "Solveig, dance," he begged.

"You were horrible then," she said and went on into the house.

Then Peer grew wilder than ever, noisier, and more drunken. And, just at that moment, the trembling, frightened, little bridegroom came in a fluster to him, distractedly shaking his head.

"Ingrid has shut herself up and locked herself in the storeroom. She will not come out to me. Peer, will you get her?" he begged.

"Come!" said Peer grimly. And off he went with the bridegroom.

Scarcely had he disappeared, when a crowd of drunken fellows headed by the big smith, Aslak, whom Peer had beaten in wrestling, came shouting for Peer to face Aslak and fight with him again.

But Ase had by this time got down from the roof where Peer had so carelessly left her. She had followed her son to the wedding and now she arrived on the green with a big stick in her hand.

"Is that son of mine here?" she cried. "Oh, how beautifully I will beat him! You shall see how I will beat him!"

"Pooh!" cried the big smith, Aslak. "Your beating will be but a gentle, little drubbing beside the one I mean to give him!"

"Beat him! Beat my Peer?" Ase at once changed her tune. "Just try it, smith, if you dare! You'll feel my stick on your head!"

Shrieks interrupted their parley. Breathless, the little bridegroom came rushing into the crowd, weak and pale with agitation.

"Father! Mother! Come!" he cried. "Peer Gynt! Peer Gynt!"

"Have you taken him from me—my Peer?" Ase interrupted.

"No! See! On the hill's brow!" The bridegroom pointed off toward a high and rocky hillside while all eyes in the farmplace turned in that one direction. And there, on the top of the hill silhouetted against the sky was Peer, bearing off in his arms Ingrid, the bride-to-be! "He shouldered her and carried her off as I would carry a pig," lamented the unhappy bridegroom.

"See how he scales
that sheer cliff. He climbs
like a goat," cried the smith.
   "You beast! O would you might fall!"
Ase shook her fist at her son. But seeing him
at that moment mounting a slippery precipice,
she screamed in terror, "Take care, son! O take care!"
   "I'll have his life for this," said Ingrid's father grimly.
   "That you won't," said Ase, "for I will never let you!"

THE TREASURE CHEST

High up hill after hill to the high, white mountain-tops Peer carried Ingrid with him; but, when he had got her there, what did he want with the girl? He didn't want Ingrid really. He had only carried her off for the sheer love of adventure and because he was hurt by Solveig. Well then, he would leave her. True she loved him dearly and he had ruined her life since she could not now marry Mads Moen, but what of that for Peer? He couldn't bother to think of anyone but himself. He must always do as he pleased. That was his business in life. Let Ingrid bear her own troubles. She didn't have beautiful hair that swam like gold as did Solveig. Brutally Peer told Ingrid that he was going to leave her. Still in her wedding finery, the poor little bride begged pitifully that he should not desert her. Peer only shrugged his shoulders and went down the mountain path. He left her to make her way home, however she might be able, to face her angry father and the jeers of the neighbors alone.

Well, anyhow, Peer was free! He had all life before him for good times and adventure. Of course, he was now an outlaw. All the men in the parish would be out after him with either a gun or a stick if he ever showed his face again down there near Ingrid's home. But God would look after him. Peer had a comforting faith that he was the one supreme object of God's ever-watchful care. All things would come right for him—he was sure of that!

He ran over mountain moorlands beneath the great, glistening snowpeaks till he fell in with three pretty farmmaids. Soon he was dancing with them, forgetting even Solveig in the gaiety of the moment. Oh, but he was merry! He danced with the girls until evening when he grew tired of the fun, then he ran off alone.

And now he went wandering on through a land of great sighing trees, with stars shining bright through the leaves and shadows dappling the woodland. All at once a woman's figure appeared in the path before him. By the shimmering light of the stars, Peer saw a Green-Clad Woman. Here was luck for a youth!

"Who are you?" he demanded. "I am in need of a wife."

"I am the Dovre-King's daughter," said the Green-Clad One.

Oh, well, if she bragged like that, he could tell a better story. "My mother is Queen Ase," promptly lied Peer in reply.

"My palace is enormous," boasted the Green-Clad One.

"My mother's palace is larger," Peer swaggered brazenly.

Then the Green-Clad One spoke a line as though propounding a riddle: "*Foul it seems fair, and black it seems white.*"

"*Big it seems small, and filthy seems bright,*" Peer completed the rhyme at once. He had spoken a magic password! The Green-Clad One, at his words, fell straightway on his neck.

"Ah, Peer," she said, "now see how amazingly we fit. Bridal steed, come!" she shrieked, her shrill voice echoing far over the barren hillside. At once, a huge pig appeared. With an old sack for a saddle and a piece of rope for a bridle, he came rushing up to the woman. Peer went wild with excitement; he leaped on the back of the pig and put the Green-Clad One up before him.

"Gee-up! Gee-up!" he cried and they galloped off into the night.

THE TREASURE CHEST

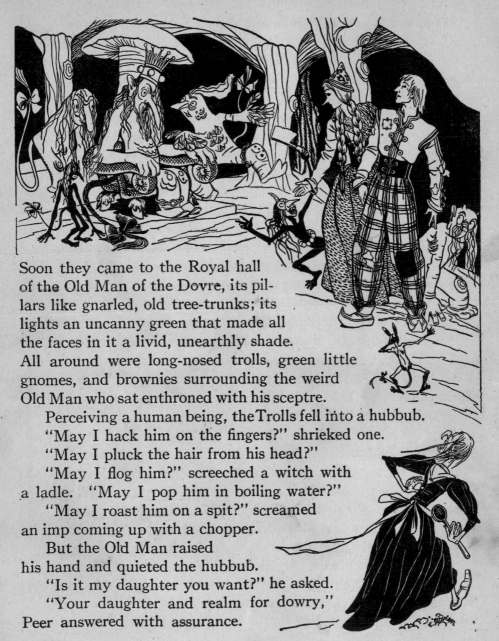

Soon they came to the Royal hall
of the Old Man of the Dovre, its pil-
lars like gnarled, old tree-trunks; its
lights an uncanny green that made all
the faces in it a livid, unearthly shade.
All around were long-nosed trolls, green little
gnomes, and brownies surrounding the weird
Old Man who sat enthroned with his sceptre.

Perceiving a human being, the Trolls fell into a hubbub.

"May I hack him on the fingers?" shrieked one.

"May I pluck the hair from his head?"

"May I flog him?" screeched a witch with
a ladle. "May I pop him in boiling water?"

"May I roast him on a spit?" screamed
an imp coming up with a chopper.

But the Old Man raised
his hand and quieted the hubbub.

"Is it my daughter you want?" he asked.

"Your daughter and realm for dowry,"
Peer answered with assurance.

"You shall have half my realm as long as I live," said the King, "and when I die, I promise that I will leave to you all my kingdom."

"I'm content," cried Peer with his swagger.

"Ah, but you, too, have some promises which you must make to me," the Old Man was very serious. "First, you must promise never to heed roads that lead out of this kingdom. You must ever shun the sunshine and deeds that are done in the day."

"Only call me King and I promise," Peer agreed at once.

"And now answer me this riddle: how do men differ from trolls?"

"Not much," answered Peer. "Big trolls want to roast you and small trolls want to scratch you. That's very much like men."

"True," replied the King. "Yet, there is this distinction. Men say: 'Be thyself!' While we say here in our world: 'Troll, to thyself be *enough*.' Do you understand the difference?"

Peer scratched his head and looked foolish. It all sounded hazy to him. He wanted to be himself, that was what he lived for! Well, trolls each found himself, without thought of anyone else, enough, enough, enough. What was the difference there?

"And now," said the weird Old Man. "I'll show you how we live down here." He summoned two trolls with pig's heads, each wearing a little white nightcap, who brought in food and drink.

"Cows give cake for us and bullocks give ale," he said.

Peer found this very strange and he didn't like the food at all.

"Next," said the Old Man, "you must throw off your Christian dress. Everything you wear here must be troll-made in our mountains except the silk bow on the end of your tail."

"I've no tail!" cried Peer indignantly.

"You must get one like all the rest! Lord Chamberlain," he called, "bring this man my Sunday-best tail."

"I won't wear a tail!" cried Peer. "I refuse to look a fool!"

"Whosoever woos my child must have a tail," said the King. "I must make you a mannerly wooer. Now this is a very fine tail with a beautiful orange bow. To let you wear it is an honor."

"Well," said Peer, giving in. "Old proverbs say that the easiest way is always to follow the custom."

So he let the Lord Chamberlain tie on the tail.

"Just try with what grace you can swing it and wag it," one of the courtiers cried.

And now the Old Man of the Dovre ordered music and dancing.

" 'Tis monstrous queer," said Peer, "I seem to see a cow playing the fiddle with her hoof and a sow in socks tripping and dancing."

"Eat him," cried one of the courtiers. "He sees a cow and a sow! He sees a cow and a sow instead of our lovely troll-maidens!"

"Let me tear off an ear," a ferocious troll-maiden shrieked, while the Green-Clad One wept at hearing such words from her lover.

Then the Old Man said, "Bear in mind he has only human senses; but we will soon cure that. I'll just scratch each of his eyes then he nevermore will be plagued with seeing a cow and a sow dancing in this hall. His bride will look beautiful to him."

True to his words, the King laid out some sharp instruments.

"But, if I let you make a scratch in my eyes," said Peer, "when will it ever happen that I get back the sight of men?"

"Never!" said the Troll-King promptly.

"Then the bargain's off!" cried Peer. "I'm willing to give up my breeches, wear a tail, and swear that a cow is a beautiful maid; but I can't agree never to be myself as a man again."

"Very well," said the Old Man, looking at Peer with disdain. "It's really a pity, though. You'd make a fine troll, I'm sure! But, since you have chosen this way, my children, dash him to pieces." Immediately all the troll-imps began to pinch and hit Peer.

"Ow!" Peer screeched in terror and tried to bolt up the chimney. The imps bit him from behind. He made for the cellar door. The imps were there before him. He tried to crawl down a mousehole. The trolls ran and covered it up. One little imp bit his ear, others made for his eyes. Jeering with hatred and malice, they whirled in a frenzied orgy around their terrified victim. They swarmed like hornets over him until he fell to the floor and lay there buried deep in a squirming heap of imps.

"Help, mother, I die!" he cried. "Solveig, throw your prayer book at them." He was half-swooning in anguish.

Then, from very far off there came a faint ringing and pealing. Holy sound of church bells! Ase and Solveig were searching in the mountains for their loved one. Fearing he might have fallen into the hands of trolls, they had set the church bells ringing.

At sound of those bells, the trolls fled in a mighty uproar of yelling and screaming and screeching. The Hall of the Old Man collapsed and Peer was left in pitch darkness. Then a voice cried, "He was too strong! There were women behind him."

"The Hall of the Mountain King," by Grieg, shows the trolls in full cry after Peer. Bassoons weirdly describe their antics as they circle jeering at Peer. Excitement increases to the final crash when the hall disappears.

THE TREASURE CHEST

Dull and heavy-eyed, Peer came to himself again. Alone, he wandered off into the depths of the pinewoods. He was now an outlaw. He could not go back to his home. Well, here in this deep pinewoods, he must build a house. When he was able to work, he set about felling trees and, at last, his hut stood finished with reindeer horns over the roof to bring the place good luck. One day, the snow lay deep covering the hills and valleys and weighing down the pine trees. Peer was out in front fastening a bar to his door to keep the troll-folk out, when suddenly, he looked up and saw Solveig coming to him gliding swiftly on snowshoes.

"Solveig," he cried in delight. "It cannot be! Yes, it is Solveig! And you dare trust yourself to come here alone to me!"

"I was called by your longing for me and by my longing for you," Solveig answered gently. "Life stifled me down in the valley."

"But your father and mother! Your little sister!" cried Peer.

"I have now no one on earth I call father, mother, or sister. I have left them all for you," said Solveig.

"My Solveig! My own dear!" Peer was overwhelmed with joy.

"Henceforth you must be my all," Solveig trusted him wholly.

"But do you know that a decree was passed against me? I have forfeited all my heritage and have only this hut for my own!"

"Think you I left my people for your farm and heritage?" Solveig cried. "For you only I sped here on snowshoes and, when the people I met asked me where I was going, I always answered 'Home.'"

"Now I can throw away locks!" Peer was in a transport. "If you dare dwell with me, the hut will be so blessed no troll can ever enter. Solveig, let me look at you. How fair you are! How pure! Let me lift you up. Oh, you are light as a feather. How I have longed for you, dear! This hut, I must tear it down. I'll build a finer one that shall shine with brass from afar."

"Nay, dear," said Solveig softly. "All here is to my liking. I can breathe at this height. Mid this soughing of fir trees, what stillness and what song! Here I am in my home."

"Solveig, are you sure? Will you stay with me, forever?"

"The path I have taken here will never lead back," said Solveig.

"Mine!" cried Peer exulting. "Go into the house, my beloved. I must fetch wood for the fire and you shall sit warm beside it." He opened the door for her and watched as she entered the house. Then he laughed for joy and gave a great leap into the air.

But, as he moved off after wood, a figure arose before him.

"Good evening, Peer," said an ugly old woman in green.

"Who's there?" Peer demanded gruffly.

"A woman you once wooed. I live quite close," she answered.

"You troll-snout! What a horror!" It was the Green-Clad One!

"You need only turn the girl from your door, then I'll lose my snout, my love. But I'll give you up to no one."

"Begone!" cried Peer in a rage.

"Go away, Peer? No, not I. I'll come every day," said the hag. "I'll make a third at your hearth whenever you sit with the girl." And she vanished into the forest.

"Solveig, my maid of pure gold!" Peer was in deep despair.

THE TREASURE CHEST

Alone in the snow he wrestled. All his sins came before him; his brutal adventure in carrying Ingrid off, his careless dancing with the farm girls, his wooing of the Green-Clad One when he had no love in his heart, and his willingness to give up everything which he had once held good to be King in the realm of the trolls—all these sins arose and separated him from Solveig. Hazily he knew there must be some straight road to lead him out of his troubles. There was something about being sorry, but he could not recall what it was. "There is never a straight way through this to the place where she stands," he said. Roundabout was ever his way. He could not go in and face Solveig.

"Are you coming in?" called Solveig, appearing at the door.

"No," he answered dully. "I've something heavy to fetch."

"Then I'll come and help you," said Solveig.

"Stay where you are," he cried. "I must bear this burden alone."

"But don't go too far away, Peer."

"Be patient, dear, and wait, whether I go far or near!"

"I will wait," said Solveig. "I will wait for you here."

Leaving her in the doorway, Peer plunged into the woods.

And now in the depths of his trouble, Peer longed to see his mother. But what did he find at home? Little, old Ase was dying, lonely and forlorn. All her goods had been sold to pay for the pranks of her son. For a moment the heart of Peer was struck with love and repentance. He sat by the old woman's bed and played with her once again as they had played in his childhood. But, while they played, Ase died. "Let her funeral be fine!" Peer cried to a neighbor, leaving no money, however, to make that funeral fine.

Out into the world went Peer to escape those who hunted him. Months passed into years while he wandered all the world over. Great loads of money he made in schemes by no means honest; and, when he was middle-aged, he put all his gold on a yacht and started out for Greece. He would join the Turkish tyrants who

"Ase's Death," the second number in Grieg's *Peer Gynt Suite*, is a sombre dirge, gloomy and haunting. It depicts the lonely and forlorn old mother as she lies dying, deserted by her harum-scarum son.

were oppressing Greece. He would make himself King of Greece, then emperor of the world! But some strangers he invited to join him in his adventure, made off with his ship and his money leaving Peer stranded on the shore amid the palm groves of Morocco.

But he said to himself, as usual, "God will look after me!"

He would be a prophet if he could not be an emperor, so he prayed for a horse to ride to some distant, desirable land. As if in answer to prayer, he suddenly heard a horse neighing and, following the sound to a cave, he found a richly caparisoned horse, a pile of shining jewels, and some finely-embroidered robes hidden there by a thief who had stolen them from an emperor. Well, that was all he needed. God had helped him as he should! He put on the robes, took the jewels, and rode off over the sands.

When he came in all his glory to a little green oasis hidden away in the desert, the people took him for a prophet, appearing as if by magic, and they all bowed low before him. "The prophet is come!" they sang. "To us, to us, he is come!" Soon he had a tent where he could lie back on soft cushions, smoke a long pipe, and drink coffee while dancing girls danced before him. Anitra was the prettiest of the dancing girls, graceful and lithe as a snake.

"Anitra's Dance," the third number of the *Peer Gynt Suite*, is a mazurka portraying the agility, grace, and suppleness of Anitra. The use of the triangle, with the string instruments, gives it Oriental color and flavor.

THE TREASURE CHEST

Well, Peer was now middle-aged, but after all, he thought, not too old to charm a pretty girl. He offered jewels to Anitra and Anitra took them gladly. She told Peer how wise he was, how great and how wonderful! One day Peer took her on his horse and rode with her into the desert. There she got his last jewel, then seizing his horse, she cut him maliciously with her whip and rode off with mocking words.

Peer was thunderstruck. He had thought himself irresistible. And while he stood there alone, deserted in those hot sands by that mischievous little baggage who had wanted only his jewels, back in the cool, green north Solveig, fair and comely though she was a middle-aged woman, sat at her spinning in the sunshine before the hut he had built, waiting for him still, faithful as she had promised. And she sang as she turned her wheel:

"You will come home some day. That I know! That I know!
And I will wait for you, dear, for at parting I promised you so."*

Well, Peer didn't think of her. He forgot while she remembered. He squandered while she treasured. And he said to save his pride, "After all, perhaps, I wasn't really meant for a prophet. I was cut out to be a scholar. So I'll just go off to Egypt and seek out the secret of the Sphinx. Then in time men will say, 'There goes the great Peer Gynt! He knows more than any man.'"

The Sphinx couldn't tell him anything, not really, of course! He knew it all anyway! After all, the height of wisdom was for a man to be himself and didn't he know that already? Hadn't he always done just as he pleased? He knew as much as the Sphinx. But, as he stood by the Sphinx in sight of the tall minarets of Cairo, boasting of all he knew, a strange man suddenly sprang out from behind the statue.

"Ha," said he. "You're just the man I've been looking for. I belong to a very large group who have dared to be just themselves. Come with me. We will make you our King." And he

---

* "Solveig's Song" by Grieg, is a beautiful song of spring sung by Solveig as she sits spinning before the hut where she has waited so long. Peer will return like spring, and she will wait for him as she promised.

dragged Peer off to Cairo to the courtyard of a large building.

"At last, I shall be King among men of wisdom!" thought Peer.

But, when he looked about him, he found himself locked in a mad-house with crazy people in cages shrieking all about.

"Now you're in the only place where men can be themselves without thought of anyone else," his crazy companion cried. "We ride in full sail as ourselves. No one here has tears for the sorrow of anyone else. No one listens here to anything others think. We shriek our own thoughts to the winds and each to himself is enough."

Peer was dizzy with terror. He ran to get out of the place. Well now he had no money. He must begin all over again to provide himself with riches. So he dug for gold in California, he went into the seal-catching business in the cold lands of Hudson Bay. He worked for many years until he was an old man. Well, what did he have now? Plenty of gold, indeed, but no one at all to love him. A longing for home came on him, so he gathered his riches together and boarded a ship for Norway. In a raging storm, he approached once more the frowning cliffs of his homeland.

"Poor old Peer," he thought, very sorry now for himself. "There is no one to welcome him home."

Close by the land among rocks, Peer's ship was wrecked in the tempest. He was washed overboard, all his riches again were lost. And, when he came to the surface, it was only by pushing another man off the small boat to which he clung that he, himself, gained the land. Penniless now and old, he wandered in the darkness over a barren heath where forest fires had been burning. Charred tree trunks rose black and ugly and white mists rolled about. In such a dreary spot, Peer could not avoid thinking of all the lies he had told. Ghostly bits of thistledown, floating by on the wind seemed to cry out and say, "We are thoughts you should have thought!" Dewdrops dripping from branches said, "We're tears you should have shed!" And broken straws seemed to murmur, "We are deeds you should have done!"

THE TREASURE CHEST

Then all at once in the darkness, a figure loomed before Peer. It was a button-molder bearing a casting ladle such as Peer himself had once played with when he melted tin as a boy and made it into buttons, stamped with some childish design.

"Peer," said the Button-molder, "I have come for you."

"What for?" demanded Peer.

"You must go into the ladle. You were meant for a button to shine on the coat of the world, but you have defied the design life meant to stamp on you. So, like all other spoiled goods, you must go into the wastebox and be melted up with the mass."

In spite of himself, Peer paled. "You don't mean to mix me up with Tom, Dick, and Harry and make me anew!" he cried.

"That's just what I mean," said the Button-molder. "You have talked much of being yourself, but never in all your life have you really been yourself. Really to be yourself means to display like a signboard our Master's design upon you."

Peer was now all at once beside himself with fright. He begged at least for delay, a chance somehow to make good the errors of his life. But the Button-molder replied, "I will wait until the next crossroad. If, when you meet me there, you can bring me a list of your sins, perhaps we can change your sentence."

Peer wandered off in terror. How was he ever to get a list of his sins together, he who had never thought enough of any wrong he did to remember it over night? The awful old troll-king rose up to mock him. "You should really have stayed with me and become a troll," the Old Man said. "For all your life, you've lived as a troll. You've thought of no one but yourself. You've been to yourself enough. And, that, as you remember, is the motto of the trolls."

A hill-troll, sure enough! That was what he had been. Peer went on in a frenzy. Twice at the crossroads he begged for delay but the Button-molder replied, "The third time we meet, I will take you!"

Just at that moment, Peer saw a light shine out of a cottage. In his agony he ran toward it. Day now began to dawn and he saw a pair of reindeer horns touched with the sun's first light. What was this house before him? It was the hut he had built and, inside, a woman was singing.

"Solveig!" cried Peer. "Here! The list of my sins is with her!"

He took a step toward the door and then the old argument

THE TREASURE CHEST

came. "Roundabout. Turn aside!" But this time he answered boldly, "No! I shall go straight through, however hard the way."

At that moment Solveig came out, a sweet-appearing old woman bound with her hymn book for church. At sight of Peer, she cried. "Praise be the Lord! It is he! I knew that he would come."

"All my sins cry out to thee, Solveig." Peer threw himself down before her. But she put her hand on his head.

"Oh, my own lad," she said. "In naught hast thou sinned to me. Thou hast made my life as a beautiful song. Blessed be thou at this meeting." She sat down beside him on the threshold.

"But where, all this time, has my real self been, the one that bears God's design?" Peer cried out for understanding.

"In my faith, in my hope, in my love," Solveig answered simply.

A light came into Peer's eyes. "Oh, hide me in thy faith and love!" He buried his face in her lap and clung to her like a child.

Solveig sang to him softly:

"Sleep, dearest boy of mine,
I will cradle thee. I will guard thee."

And the Button-molder, lurking in the pinewoods, now knew he would never get Peer, for the man's deep love for Solveig—the only real thing in his life—had awakened him at last. Now he would recognize wrong when he was prompted to do it. Now his world would include others as well as himself. No longer would he live like a troll unto himself enough. He would not be at the crossroad. At last he would truly live.

Peer Gynt is based on an old Norse folk tale, but Ibsen, one of Norway's greatest dramatists, made it, like *Faust*, a tale of man's experience in discovering what he really is—how to be truly himself.

François Villon, the Vagabond of Paris
OLIVE BEAUPRÉ MILLER

In the year 1449, a lean, sharp-faced young ragamuffin, some eighteen years old, stood on a bridge in Paris. Below him the steel gray river rushed under its countless bridges; opposite, the twin towers of Notre Dame Cathedral rose gray against the sky; and all around was the city whose life he loved so well. Narrow, winding streets! Tall, sharp-gabled houses leaning crazily together! Scrolled and painted shop-signs creaking in the wind! An arched shrine at the corner and before it brightly burning, a little swaying lamp! All the changing colors of the ever-shifting crowd, and through it all the street cries—how Master Villon loved it!

He should have been at his classes over in the University; but as usual he was rambling and doing as he pleased. A fishwife, screeching shrilly, flung a coarse joke at him. He tossed her back a jibe as good as she had given and went on idly watching. All Paris passed him by. Beggars, whining, limping, showing ugly sores; tradesmen, tumblers, showmen, quacks, and mountebanks! A lady of high station with her prancing cavalcade, an elegant cloaked dandy! Friars in black and white, and then a wedding party, marching two by two in colors like a flower-bed!

Villon, with his romantic adventures, has become the hero of the light opera, *The Vagabond King*, by Rudolf Friml. The rousing "Song of the Vagabonds," sung by Villon and his followers, remains permanently popular.

THE TREASURE CHEST

A clatter of hoofs was heard; the crowd on the bridge fell back. The Provost of Paris was passing with his body-guard of twelve archers. Suddenly in the lull François Villon saw an ugly, hag-like scarecrow, an old woman, ragged, toothless, shuffling up the street. Sharp pity smote him deep. That mumbling witch of eighty had once been a famous beauty! In his heart a song began to speak the unspeakable sorrow of that woman's vanished youth. For this ragged student of Paris was a maker of songs for the people. He sang the life of Paris, its depths, its heights, its joys, its miseries, its follies. All that great city's teeming, tumultuous, vigorous being François Villon lived and sang in the music of words.

But now as the old woman vanished, François went on his way. He set out to seek entertainment among the colorful crowd that thronged the Gingerbread Fair; but when evening shadows darkened and a squad of the night-watch passed, their weapons gleaming in the light of a smoky cresset on a street-corner, he sought a more gruesome spot. In the cemetery of the Innocents there was a Gothic arcade enclosing four sides of a square which

was filled with tombs of the dead. The arcade was lined with shops but above these in open vaults, exposed to the gaze of the crowd, lay a mass of human bones, while down the whole length of one wall was painted the Dance of Death. Stiff and grinning, stood Death behind the Lord Pope and Emperor; he clutched the Abbess by the hand; he tapped the Canon on the shoulder; he grimaced in mocking posture before the Student, the Merchant,

Danse Macabre, the dance of the skeletons, by Saint-Saëns illustrates this weird delight in the gruesome. Bones rattle to a xylophone accompaniment, the dance grows wilder till cock's crow when ghosts flee to their tombs.

the Drunkard swigging in the pot-house. Even the Imbecile, chuckling and sticking straws in his hair, discovered the companion of his gambols to be none other than Death! This ghastly cemetery had become the fashionable place for gallants to meet their ladies and the world to promenade. And thither went Villon, too, to enjoy the life of the moment and to shrug his shoulders at death.

From this gruesome promenade the student went on about midnight to the grisliest place of all, the gibbet outside the city where murderers and thieves were hung. On summer nights rowdies of Paris brought their girls out from the city for a midnight frolic by the gibbet with the bodies still dangling there and birds of prey hovering about. Something in the French nature under their outward gaiety made them flaunt at death. Perhaps it was all the miseries they had suffered for so many years when in the Hundred Years' War, the English had ravaged the land.

In the days when Villon was born the English were masters of Paris, and bands of invading Burgundians laid waste all the fields. Famine, plague, pale misery stalked the city streets; wolves in the terrible winter carried off more than one baby; and the poor, in grinding torment, lived on turnip-tops. Yet war, wolves, smallpox, famine could not kill the spirit of Paris. The people laughed and chattered at the smallest sign of blue sky; they hung absurd effigies of the English in squares and public places, and when their King, Charles VII, entered the city victorious, they lit great bonfires for joy, presented plays and gay mummeries, and began at once to recover after the fashion of Paris with her vigorous strength of life. And so at the place of the gibbet, Parisian rowdies gamboled, flaunting their high spirits in the very face of death, and François gamboled with them, sharing their life to the full.

At last he went to his home in the Latin Quarter of Paris; that conglomeration of spires and colleges and convents mixed with shops for students and little open-air bookstalls which served University life. François sneaked in very quietly so as not to arouse that grand old man, Guillaume Villon, his kinsman, with whom he lived. François was born of poor people, he had lived on the streets of Paris until his good mother, a widow, sorrowing over her poverty, and anxious for her wild son, had taken the shabby gamin from the bright adventures of the streets to the home of Guillaume Villon. Finding the child intelligent, the good old priest had adopted him. He had sent François to school in the great University of Paris; he had loved him, sheltered him, taught him, again and again forgiven him and helped him out of trouble.

But François was always in scrapes. He loved Guillaume very dearly, he loved and pitied his mother with a great compassion for the sorrow which he himself had caused her, and yet he was always wayward. His friends were pickpockets and thieves; he loved the coarse laughter and noise of the taverns where vagabonds gathered, and though he had no interest in robbing just for money, he often stole ducks by night from the waters of the city moat and played other knavish tricks to get an easy meal rather than work at copying or beg with his cap in his hand as many a poor scholar must in those hard times in Paris. His life was in making songs and in living with full completeness all there was in the life of Paris.

In June, 1455 came the Feast of Corpus Christi. Paris was decked with green branches, altars were built on the streets and tapestries hung from the windows. Processions, gay colored with banners, glowing with lighted candles, escorted the Sacred Host as it was borne through the streets beneath its golden canopy. But in the evening when the organs had ceased their mighty thundering and the altar lights were extinguished, the holiday crowd streamed out and took possession of the streets.

François ate supper at a tavern with a group of gay companions and when he was ready to leave, he came out into the night. Here and there a window glowed golden in the dusk and from the tavern came voices, merry, careless, drunken, and the stave of a raucous song. Spying a priest named Gilles and a lady named Ysabeau sitting nearby on a bench, François sat down to talk with them. But suddenly another priest by the name of Philip Chermoye appeared with a friend on the scene.

"I've found you, you rogue!" cried Philip, for he harbored a grudge against François.

Rising in great surprise François said: "What angers you?"

Giving no answer, Philip struck François such a blow that he fell back on the bench. Seeing that a fight was on, the spectators all took leave, slipping quietly into the night. A furious tussle followed and when it was over Philip lay fatally wounded on the ground. In the shop of a barber-surgeon, François got his own wounds dressed, then he took to his heels and ran.

Before the bells of Paris had begun their morning ringing, he was well beyond the walls and in the open country. Dodging about the countryside he now lived by his wits, occasionally snapping up a hen or a duck from some barnyard, grubbing turnips out of a field, running at breakneck speed to escape some indignant farmer, and always anxiously waiting for news to come from Paris. But while he was roaming the countryside, the wounded Philip died and on his deathbed forgave him. Good

THE TREASURE CHEST

Guillaume used his influence with officers of the law and after eight months' exile, François returned to Paris.

Now for a time he tried to earn a little money by copying manuscripts, but by the end of a year his position was once more desperate. He had no money in his purse and he was deeply in love with Katherine de Vausselles, who ridiculed and scorned him. Other girls in the taverns showered their favors on François, but he would have only Katherine who would have naught of him. Falling into deep gloom and bitter melancholy, François once more decided to shake off the dust of Paris.

But the night before he was to leave, being downcast and desperate, he got into another scrape. With four companions he climbed by the help of a stolen ladder over the high stone wall of one of the many colleges that formed the University. Breaking into the college, the youths forced open a chest and stole five hundred crowns, and now in good truth François was forced to leave Paris in haste. With a peddler's pack on his back he tramped the countryside, selling ribbons, laces, lute-strings, pocket-knives, and colored pictures of saints. At night he put up in a barn or slept beneath some hedgerow and so he came at last to the castle and gorgeous court of the Duke of Orleans, a clever writer himself and a patron of all the arts. Charles held open house for any man of letters and he welcomed François warmly. Already the vagabond poet was known and loved in France. Life was easy there in the castle of Charles of

Orleans; but François began to chafe. It was tedious, all so regular, the same old thing each day! His vagabond blood rose up and forced him on again.

No better was his lingering in the castle of the Duke of Bourbon. There, too, he was befriended and offered an easy life. But restraint was galling to François. He made once more for the highroad. For four whole years he wandered, now sleeping under a Duke's roof, now lying under a hedgerow. At last at Orleans, he found himself cast into prison, accused of sacrilege, and under sentence of death. Chained by the ankles in a dungeon, dark, airless, infested by toads, he was left to think on his sins and face the day of his death. But just at that time it chanced that Charles VII died and Louis XI came to the throne in France. Making a solemn progress through his new dominions, Louis entered Orleans. In honor of his coronation he set many prisoners free. Wearing his shabby old hat with its row of blessed leaden images of saints around the crown, he blinked his sardonic eyes and signed the papers of freedom for one Master François Villon.

"My kingdom," he said, "holds a hundred thousand rascals of equal rascality, but only one poet like Villon!"

Incoherent with joy, François danced a fandango in the dirty straw of his dungeon. He waved his arms and legs madly, he bellowed aloud to the roof, he frantically hugged his jailor! But though he was now released from the charges against him at Orleans, there still remained hanging over him the burglary in Paris. Everlastingly patient, good Guillaume again used his influence. It was arranged that François should repay his share of the money that had been stolen and return again to Paris. With all his old kindness Guillaume welcomed the wanderer home, a fatted goose was roasted, and with a sigh of relief, the sinner mounted the stairs that led to his old room.

THE TREASURE CHEST

Often just after this the candle burned late in that room. François was now pouring out in his poem, *The Grand Testament*, the songs that had surged in his heart for years as he wandered the highways. For his mother he wrote a beautiful little prayer to the Virgin. Tenderly he remembered that when he had caused her such grief, the Virgin had been her comfort. And in this poem, too, he expressed, with unspoken sorrow, the depth of his love for Guillaume.

> My more than father, who indeed
> To me more tenderness hath shown
> Than mothers to the babes they feed,
> Who me from many a scrape hath freed
> And now of me hath scant liesse—
> I do entreat him, bended-kneed,
> He leave me to my present stress.

But deeply though François felt the sorrow he had caused, he could not keep out of trouble. Soon he was back in the taverns with the rogues who had been his companions. When he recited at the tables to the merry clink of the wine-cups, a new Ballad in the *Jargon*, ugly faces would warm him with laughter, hairy visages seamed with scars, with a black patch over one eye, would loom up smiling from the shadows, gnarled hands would clap him on the back and refill his cup with wine.

Scarcely were his eyes dry after his apologies, his prayers and promises to Master Guillaume, when he spent an evening at a tavern drinking with three companions. As they issued out of the place they passed a magistrate's house where in the lighted windows they saw the clerks still working. Stupidly François' companions made fun of the clerks at their books. Teased into rage, the clerks came tumbling out of the house and started a noisy scrimmage. The magistrate heard the brawl. Pompously strutting forth, he ordered an end to the battle.

One of François' comrades plunged a knife in his back. Everyone then disappeared; but though François himself had taken no part in the fight, the magistrate caught sight of him just as he was fleeing and recognized his face. He was taken prisoner again and, irony of fate, after all the sins he really had committed, he was now sentenced to death for something he had not done.

Again must Guillaume Villon tread the well-worn path to his influential friends and intercede for François. Again at the eleventh hour did François escape the gallows. The sentence of death was remitted but he was ordered at once to take his leave of Paris. Blinded with tears, old Guillaume muttered his last benediction over the prodigal's head. Blinded with tears, the mother said her last good bye and lifted her gnarled old hands for comfort to the Virgin. Sadly François tramped through the narrow, crooked streets of the city he loved so well. He passed out through its gates and was never heard of more.

Idle, impulsive, mocking, he had yet worshipped beauty. Out of the depths of his closeness to the teeming life of Paris he had sung the heart of his people. The Parisians loved him dearly; and as in time his songs were sung throughout the country, they helped make the language of Paris, rather than the various dialects spoken in different districts, the language of all of France! So to François Villon does the Frenchman owe the language spoken in France today.

THE TREASURE CHEST

THE BALLAD OF EAST AND WEST
RUDYARD KIPLING

*Oh, East is East, and West is West, and
never the twain shall meet,
Till Earth and Sky stand presently at
God's great Judgment Seat;
But there is neither East nor West, Border, nor Breed, nor Birth,
When two strong men stand face to face,
though they come from the ends of
the earth!*

Ka'mal is out with twenty men to raise the Border side,
And he has lifted the Colonel's mare that is the Colonel's pride.
He has lifted her out of the stable-door between the dawn and the day,
And turned the calkins upon her feet, and ridden her far away.
Then up and spoke the Colonel's son that led a troop of the Guides:
"Is there never a man of all my men can say where Ka'mal hides?"
Then up and spoke Mo-ham'med Khan, the son of the Res'sal-dar':
"If ye know the track of the morning-mist, ye know where his pickets are.
"At dusk he harries the Ab'a-zai'—at dawn he is into Bo-nair',
"But he must go by Fort Buk-loh' to his own place to fare.

No Englishman knew India better than Rudyard Kipling, who received the Nobel prize for literature in 1907. Born in Bombay, he spent his childhood and many later years in India. See his *Jungle Book* and *Kim*.

"So if ye gallop to Fort Buk-loh' as fast as a bird can fly,
"By the favour of God ye may cut him off ere he win to the Tongue of
  Ja-gai'.
"But if he be past the Tongue of Ja-gai', right swiftly turn ye then,
"For the length and the breadth of that grisly plain is sown with Ka'mal's
  men.
"There is rock to the left, and rock to the right, and low lean thorn
  between,
"And ye may hear a breech-bolt snick, where never a man is seen."

The Colonel's son has taken a horse, and a raw rough dun was he,
With the mouth of a bell and the heart of Hell and the head of a gallows-
  tree.
The Colonel's son to the Fort has won, they bid him stay to eat—
Who rides at the tail of a Border thief, he sits not long at his meat.

He's up and away from Fort Buk-loh' as fast as he can fly,
Till he was aware of his father's mare in the gut of the Tongue of Ja-gai',
Till he was aware of his father's mare with Ka'mal upon her back,
And when he could spy the white of her eye, he made the pistol crack.

He has fired once, he has fired twice, but the whistling ball went wide.
"Ye shoot like a soldier," Ka'mal said. "Show now if ye can ride!"
It's up and over the Tongue of Ja-gai', as blown dust-devils go,
The dun he fled like a stag of ten, but the mare like a barren doe.
The dun he leaned against the bit and slugged his head above,
But the red mare played with the snaffle-bars, as a maiden plays with
  a glove.

There was rock to the left and rock to the right, and low lean thorn
  between,
And thrice he heard a breech-bolt snick tho' never a man was seen.

They have ridden the low moon out of the sky, their hoofs drum up the
  dawn,
The dun he went like a wounded bull, but the mare like a new-roused
  fawn.

THE TREASURE CHEST

The dun he fell at a water-course—
    in a woeful heap fell he,
And Ka'mal has turned the red mare
    back, and pulled the rider free.
He has knocked the pistol out of
    his hand—small room was there
    to strive,
" 'Twas only by favour of mine,"
    quoth he, "ye rode so long alive:
"There was not a rock for twenty
    mile, there was not a clump of tree,
"But covered a man of my own men
    with his rifle cocked on his knee.
"If I had raised my bridle-hand as
    I have held it low,
"The little jackals that flee so fast
    were feasting all in a row.
"If I had bowed my head on my
    breast, as I have held it high,
"The kite that whistles above us now were gorged till she could not fly."

Lightly answered the Colonel's son: "Do good to bird and beast,
"But count who come for the broken meats before thou makest a feast.
"If there should follow a thousand swords to carry my bones away,
"Belike the price of a jackal's meal were more than a thief could pay.
"They will feed their horse on the standing crop, their men on the
    garnered grain,
"The thatch of the byres will serve their fires when all the cattle are
    slain.
"But if thou thinkest the price be fair,—thy brethren wait to sup,
"The hound is kin to the jackal-spawn,—howl, dog, and call them up!
"And if thou thinkest the price be high, in steer and gear and stack,
"Give me my father's mare again, and I'll fight my own way back!"
Ka'mal has gripped him by the hand and set him upon his feet.
"No talk shall be of dogs," said he, "when wolf and grey wolf meet.
"May I eat dirt if thou has hurt of me in deed or breath;
"What dam of lances brought thee forth to jest at the dawn with Death?"

Lightly answered the Colonel's son: "I hold by the blood of my clan:
"Take up the mare for my father's gift—by God, she has carried a man!"

The red mare ran to the Colonel's son, and muzzled against his breast;
"We be two strong men," said Ka'mal then, "but she loveth the younger
    best.
"So she shall go with a lifter's dower, my turquoise-studded rein,
"My broidered saddle and saddle-cloth, and silver stirrups twain."
The Colonel's son a pistol drew, and held it muzzle-end,
"Ye have taken the one from a foe," said he; "will ye take the mate
    from a friend?"

"A gift for a gift," said Ka'mal straight; "a limb for the risk of a limb.
"Thy father has sent his son to me, I'll send my son to him!"

With that he whistled his only son, that dropped from a mountain-
    crest—
He trod the ling like a buck in spring, and he looked like a lance in rest.
"Now here is thy master," Ka'mal said, "who leads a troop of the
    Guides,
"And thou must ride at his left side as shield on shoulder rides.
"Till Death or I cut loose the tie, at camp and board and bed,
"Thy life is his—thy fate it is to guard him with thy head.
"So, thou must eat the White Queen's meat, and all her foes are thine,
"And thou must harry thy father's hold for the peace of the Borderline.
"And thou must make a trooper though and hack thy way to power—
"Belike they will raise thee to Res'sal-dar' when I am hanged in Pe-
    shawur'."
They have looked each other between the eyes, and there they found
    no fault,
They have taken the Oath of the Brother-in-Blood on leavened bread
    and salt.
They have taken the Oath of the Brother-in-Blood on fire and fresh-cut
    sod,
On the hilt and the haft of the Khyber knife, and the Wondrous Names
    of God.

THE TREASURE CHEST

The Colonel's son he rides the mare and Ka'mal's boy the dun,
And two have come back to Fort Buk-loh' where there went forth but
    one.
And when they drew to the Quarter-Guard, full twenty swords flew
    clear—
There was not a man but carried his feud with the blood of the moun-
    taineer.
"Ha' done! Ha' done!" said the Colonel's son. "Put up the steel at
    your sides!
"Last night ye had struck at a Border thief—to-night 'tis a man of the
    Guides!"

Oh, East is East, and West is West, and
    never the twain shall meet,
Till Earth and Sky stand presently at
    God's great Judgment Seat;
But there is neither East nor West, Bor-
    der, nor Breed, nor Birth,
When two strong men stand face to face,
    though they come from the ends of
    the earth!

Gideon, the Warrior

From the Book of Judges

The children of Israel did evil in the sight of the Lord; and the Lord delivered them into the hand of Mid'i-an seven years. And because of the Mid'i-an-ites, the children of Israel made them the dens which are in the mountains, and caves, and strongholds. And the Midianites came up, and the Am-a'lek-ites, and the children of the East, and they encamped against the children of Israel, and destroyed the increase of the earth, and left no sustenance for Israel, neither sheep, nor ox, nor ass. For they came up with their cattle and their tents, and they came as grasshoppers for multitude.

Then there came an angel of the Lord, and sat under an oak which was in Oph'rah, that pertained unto Jo'ash, the A'bi-ez'rite. And his son Gid'e-on threshed wheat by the winepress, to hide it

Religion inspired the first formal music from the days of the psalms and long before. The joyous rapture of thankfulness to God, the Creator, is expressed in *My Heart Ever Faithful* by Johann Sebastian Bach (1685-1750).

from the Midianites. And the angel of the Lord said unto Gideon: "The Lord is with thee, thou mighty man of valor."

And Gideon said: "Oh, my Lord, if the Lord be with us, why then is all this befallen us?"

And the Lord looked upon him and said: "Go in this thy might, and thou shalt save Israel from the hands of the Midianites. Have not I sent thee?"

And Gideon said unto the angel: "Oh, my Lord, wherewith shall I save Israel? Behold my family is poor in Ma-nas'seh, and I am the least in my father's house."

And the Lord said unto him: "Surely I will be with thee and thou shalt smite the Midianites as one man."

Then Gideon said unto the angel: "Depart not hence, I pray thee, until I bring forth my present and set it before thee."

And the angel said: "I will tarry until thou come again."

And Gideon went in and made ready a kid and unleavened cakes of an ephah of flour; the flesh he put in a basket and he put the broth in a pot and brought it out unto the angel under the oak and presented it.

And the angel of God said unto him: "Take the flesh and the unleavened cakes and lay them upon this rock and pour out the broth."

And Gideon did so. Then the angel of the Lord put forth the end of the staff that was in his hand and touched the flesh and the unleavened cakes and there rose up fire out of the rock and consumed the flesh and the unleavened cakes. And the angel of the Lord departed out of his sight.

Then all the Midianites and the Amalekites and the children of the East were gathered together and pitched in the valley of Jez're-el. But the Spirit of the Lord came upon Gideon, and he blew a trumpet; and A'bi-e'zer was gathered after him; and he sent messengers throughout all Ma-nas'seh and unto Ash'er and Zeb'u-lun and Naph'ta-li; and they came up to join him.

And Gideon said unto God: "If thou wilt save Israel by mine hand, as thou has said, show me a sign. Tonight will I put a fleece of wool on the ground and in the morning if the dew be on the fleece only, and it be dry upon all the earth beside, then shall I know that thou wilt save Israel by mine hand, as thou hast said."

And it was so, for he rose up early on the morrow and wringed the dew out of the fleece, a bowl full of water.

And Gideon said again unto God: "Let not thine anger be hot against me! Yet let me prove, I pray thee, but this once more with the fleece. Let it now be dry upon the fleece, and upon all the ground let there be dew."

And God did so that night; for it was dry upon the fleece only in the morning and there was dew on all the ground.

Then Gideon and all the people that were with him rose up early, and pitched beside the well of Ha'rod; so that the host of the Midianites were on the north side of them, by the hill of Mo'reh, in the valley.

And the Lord said unto Gideon:

"The people that are with thee are too many for me to give the Midianites into their hands, lest Israel fail to recognize strength cometh from the Lord, lest they vaunt themselves against me saying, 'Mine *own* hand hath saved me.' Now therefore, go! Proclaim in the ears of the people saying, 'Whosoever is fearful and afraid, let him return and depart early from Mount Gil'e-ad'."

But though there returned of the people two and twenty

thousand fearful ones, there yet remained ten thousand ready for the battle.

And the Lord said unto Gideon: "The people are still too many. Bring them down unto the water and I will test them for thee there. And it shall be that of whom I say unto thee, 'This shall go with thee,' the same shall go with thee; and of whomsoever I say unto thee, 'The same shall not go with thee,' the same shall not go."

So he brought down the people unto the water and the Lord said unto Gideon: "Every one that lappeth of the water with his tongue, as a dog lappeth, him shalt thou set by himself; likewise everyone that boweth down upon his knees to drink."

And the number of them that lapped, putting their hand to their mouth, were three hundred men. But all the rest of the people bowed down upon their knees to drink water.

And the Lord said unto Gideon: "By the three hundred men that lapped will I save you and deliver the Midianites into thine hand. Let the other people go, every man unto his place."

So the people took victuals in their hand, and their trumpets, and he sent all the rest of Israel every man unto his tent, and retained but those three hundred men only. And the host of Midian was beneath him in the valley.

And it came to pass the same night, that the Lord said unto Gideon: "Arise, get thee down unto the host; for I have delivered it into thine hand. But if thou fear to go down, take with thee Phu'rah, thy servant. And thou shalt hear what they say in the camp of the Midianites and thus shall thine hand be strengthened to go down against the host."

Then went Gideon down with Phurah his servant unto the outside of the armed men that were in the host. And the Midianites and the Amalekites and all the children of the East lay along in the valley like grasshoppers for multitude; and their

camels were without number, as the sand by the seaside for multitude.

And when Gideon was come, behold! there was a man that told a dream unto his fellow, and said: "Behold! I dreamed a dream, and lo! a cake of barley bread tumbled into the host of Midian, and came unto a tent and smote it that it fell, and overturned it that the tent lay along."

And his fellow answered and said: "This is nothing else save the sword of Gideon, the son of Joash, a man of Israel; for into his hand hath God delivered Midian and all the host."

And it was so when Gideon heard the telling of the dream, and the interpretation thereof, that he worshipped and returned unto the host of Israel and said: "Arise, for the Lord hath delivered into your hand the host of Midian."

And he divided the three hundred men into three companies, and he put a trumpet in every man's hand, with empty pitchers and torches within the pitchers. And he said unto them: "Look on me and do likewise. And behold! when I come to the outside of the camp it shall be that, as I do, so shall ye do. When I blow a trumpet, I and all that are with me, then blow ye the trumpets also on every side of all the camp, and say, '*The Sword of the Lord and of Gideon!*' "

So Gideon and the hundred men that were with him came unto the outside of the camp in the beginning of the middle watch, and they had but newly set the watch. And they blew the trumpets and brake the pitchers that were in their hands. And the three companies blew the trumpets and brake the pitchers that were in their hands. They held the torches in their left hands and the trumpets in their right hands to blow withal. And they cried, "*The Sword of the Lord and of Gideon!*"

THE TREASURE CHEST

And they stood every man in his place round about the camp and the Midianites hearing the noise, suddenly seeing the torches flashing out of the darkness, thought themselves surrounded by an host come up against them. They scattered in all directions and the children of Israel shouted and put them all to flight. And the three hundred blew the trumpets and in that great confusion the Lord set every man's sword among the Midianites against the sword of his fellows and the hosts of Midian fled. And the men of Israel gathered themselves together and pursued after the Midianites and drove them out of the land.

Then the men of Israel said unto Gideon: "Rule thou over us, both thou and thy son, and thy son's son also, for thou hast delivered us from the hand of Midian."

And Gideon said unto them: "I will not rule over you, neither shall my son rule over you; the Lord shall rule over you."

Thus was Midian subdued before the children of Israel, so that they lifted up their heads no more. And the country was in quietness forty years in the days of Gideon.

The Adventures of Perseus
A Greek Myth

THERE dwelt once in Argos a King's daughter named Dan'a-e and her infant son, Per'se-us. Now Ac-ris'i-us, the father of Danae, had one day been terrified half out of his wits by the words of an oracle which solemnly declared that the child of his daughter, Danae, should be the cause of his death. Thereafter, blindly accepting the words of the oracle as true, and heeding naught but his own foolish fears, Acrisius caused Danae and her son to be seized out of the strong tower wherein he had confined them, shut fast in an iron-bound chest, and cast into the sea.

Up and down on the boundless deep rocked the chest, now borne high aloft on the crest of a giant wave, and now plunged headlong down into the foaming trough of the sea. Within, Danae held close her babe and prayed to be delivered. Out and out they drifted, far and far and far. At last the waters heaved them up onto the shore of an island, and the chest was entangled fast in a fisherman's net.

Now the fisherman was amazed when he drew up out of the sea an iron-bound box, and found it to contain a young mother and child of marvelous beauty. Straightway he led them to his own cottage and commended them to the care of his wife. It then appeared that the name of the island, whereon they had been cast, was Ser'i-phus, and the fisherman was Dic'tys, no less a personage than brother to King Pol-y-dec'tes himself. In the cottage of Dictys and his good wife, Danae and her son were sheltered till Perseus grew to manhood.

Then it chanced one day that Polydectes cast his eyes on Danae and determined to have her for his queen. But Danae would have none of Polydectes, for he was a tyrant both wicked and cruel. By this time Perseus was grown a youth of such

Popular musical compositions, with Greek subjects, are *Narcissus*, by Ethelbert Nevin and the opera, *Orfeo*, by Gluck, with the beautiful "Dance of the Happy Spirits," when Orpheus, god of music, visits the underworld.

strength and promise that he was well able to defend his mother, and Polydectes perceived that if he would worry the lovely Danae into becoming his bride, he must rid himself of her stalwart son. Therefore he called to him the young Perseus and said:

"Youth, you have found in my kingdom an asylum and a home from the days of your infancy. Now that you are grown to manhood, it is but meet that you should repay the courtesy thus extended to you. You have reached the age when men of valor go venturing, to rid the world of monsters. Go you, therefore, in quest of the gorgon, Med-u′sa, who lays waste all the surrounding countryside, and show your face no more within my kingdom until you bring to me her head."

Now Perseus withdrew from the presence of King Polydectes almost in despair. He would have shrunk from no ordinary adventure possible to a hero, but the gorgons, as he knew full well, were the most hideous monsters in the world. Three terrible sisters they were, hateful, venomous, cruel. They had faces like women, but their bodies were those of beasts, all covered with scales of brass and iron so hard that no sword could pierce them; enormous were their wings and they gleamed with sinister flash of golden feathers; they had tusks instead of teeth, and sharp, cruel, brazen claws. Their hair was writhing serpents that would curl and twist and hiss, and dart out long, forked tongues to sting. Worst of all, so hard and cold and hateful was their stare, that he who looked full in their faces froze immediately into stone.

"Now how," mused Perseus, "is a man to give battle to such horrid creatures when he may not even look on them?"

Nevertheless, he bade a sad farewell to his mother and wandered along the shore lost in sorrowful thoughts and longing for some wise counsel. Suddenly there glowed about him a light seven times brighter than the sun. He looked up in amazement

and lo! there before him, resting lightly on the sand, stood a beautiful woman in long white robes with a shining helmet on her head, a staff in her hand, and a shield on her arm—Min-er'va, the goddess of Wisdom herself.

"Perseus," said she, "take this shield. So brightly is it polished that if you keep your eyes fixed upon it, you will see the gorgons reflected therein, and can give them battle without ever needing to look in their faces."

With a mighty leaping of his heart, Perseus gave thanks, yet he said: "Though I look in the shield, where shall I find among mortals a sword that can pierce through their heavy scales?"

Even as he spoke, there came a slight rustling through the air, and hovering there on his other side appeared a youth with winged sandals and cap, in one hand a winged staff about which two serpents were twined, and in the other a crooked sword that shone like a flame.

"You shall use my sword," said the youth, for he was Mer'-cu-ry, messenger from O-lymp'us, whence came the help of the gods to men who had deserved it.

THE TREASURE CHEST

Then Minerva bade the young Perseus seek out the Three Gray Sisters, cousins of the gorgons, and force from them the secret of where the Gorgons' Isle lay. Guided by Mercury, Perseus made off.

Far, far to westward he journeyed, till he came to a barren desolate shore where was everlasting twilight. Gray was the sky and gray were the giant rocks; gray were the straggling trunks of the leafless trees and gray was the misty sea. As the two approached the place, there loomed up before them three old hags in flowing gray robes with unkempt white locks hanging over their shoulders, scarce to be told from the great gray waves with crests of white that came dashing up on the shore. Perseus perceived that these three old hags possessed but one tooth and one eye among them. These they passed about from one to another and each in turn clapped the tooth into her toothless gums, and the eye into a socket in her forehead. As Perseus and Mercury groped their way cautiously towards them, it became apparent

that the old hags were just at that moment quarreling over whose turn it was to have the eye. One held the brilliant orb gleaming in her hand, and all were scolding, gesticulating, screeching. Thus, the while they wrangled, not one of the three could see at all.

"Quick," whispered Mercury to Perseus. "Now is your chance. Seize the eye and do not return it till they tell you the secret. They will never tell you otherwise."

In a flash Perseus stepped

forward, nimbly seized the eye, and withdrew again to a little distance.   Then there burst forth a perfect storm from the three old hags, for each thought the other had snatched the eye, but Perseus cried out boldly:

"I have your eye —I, a youth from beyond the seas, nor will I return it until you tell me where lies the Island of the Gorgons."

The old hags begged and whined and scolded; they tried to grope their way stealthily to him to snatch back the eye unawares, but Perseus kept well out of reach and held firm.   So at last they told him that he must go still farther westward, and there seek out certain nymphs who kept a pair of winged sandals, a magic pouch and a wonderful helmet that could render its wearer invisible. These nymphs would direct him just how to reach the Island of the Gorgons.

At that Perseus gave the Gray Women back their eye and with Mercury journeyed once more forward.   In good time they reached a beautiful glade in the forest, where the sunlight filtered in blotches of gold through the leaves, and a group of graceful nymphs with wreaths and garlands of flowers disported themselves about the banks of a clear, blue pool.   To them Perseus presented himself and told his tale.   At once they hushed their mirth and musical laughter.

"We will gladly aid the hero who goes forth to conquer the gorgon, Medusa," they cried, and they tripped lightly away, brought back the winged sandals and bound them on Perseus' feet.   About his neck they hung the magic pouch, and placed on his head the helmet of darkness.   When they had thus provided him, they pointed out the Island of the Gorgons lying low, like a bank of dun gray clouds, on the dim horizon.

Now in his winged sandals Perseus could mount up into the air as safely as Mercury.   Far, far up he soared, cleaving the air like a bird, now skimming over the chequered green earth that lay spread out far below, and now over the shining blue sea. It was midnight when Perseus at length heard a calm voice speak by his side, grave, yet melodious and mild.

"There below," it said, "lies the Island of the Gorgons." And now it was not Mercury who spoke, but Minerva, come once more in the hour of need to give Perseus counsel. Wrapped from sight in the helmet of darkness, Perseus sank downward. The moon was flooding the earth with silver, and he saw below him a rocky coast, stone, stone, everywhere stone, shining white and cold in the cold, white light. Suddenly from among the black shadows at the base of a barren cliff, there flashed a baleful gleam, and he knew it must be a moonbeam cast back from the horrid scales on the backs of the gorgons. Boldly he descended thither.

"Be cautious," said Minerva, "look into your shield."

Then in the full-glowing light of the moon, he looked into his shield and behold! a hideous sight — the three hateful sisters fast asleep, their scales and golden wings glistening, their brazen claws outspread as though ready to clutch, the snakes on their heads writhing even in sleep, and hissing now and again. Even as he looked, one of the dreadful creatures moved as though to awake.

"That is Medusa," said Minerva, "strike on the instant and do not miss your first stroke."

In a flash Perseus obeyed. The gorgon opened her freezing eyes, but Perseus, looking ever into the shield, cleaved off the

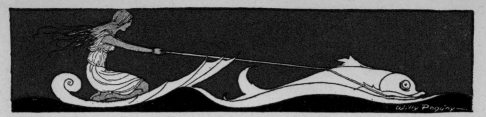

head with a single stroke of his sword, seized it, snakes and all, and dropped it into the magic pouch.

"Well done," cried Mercury.

"Now fly," said Minerva, "for the others are awakening."

On his winged sandals, Perseus sped swiftly upward, but not a moment too soon. Medusa's sisters, awakened by the noise of his stroke, perceived what had been done, and flew in a frenzy of rage to the shore, every snake on their heads a-bristle with fury. He could hear the rushing of their wings, the rattle of their brazen claws, the hissing of the serpents, as they mounted up into the air in pursuit. But, thanks to the helmet of darkness, he was hidden from their sight and made off from them in safety.

Perseus then bade farewell to Mercury and Minerva and set out alone to return to Seriphus. But it chanced on the way that he passed through the country of E-thi-o'pi-a, which was ruled over by King Ceph'e-us. Now there was come up at this time out of the deep a terrible sea monster, that ravaged the coast of Ethiopia, a huge, scaly creature with wings like a dragon and a tail like a fish. It came up and carried off oxen and people, and even destroyed whole villages. The men of Ethiopia had done all in their power to rid themselves of the monster, but in vain —there was not one among them able to stand before him. Then came forward a wise old man of the people and said:

"Lo! our queen, Cass-i-o-pe'i-a, swelled with pride of her own beauty, did boast herself lovelier than the sea-nymphs that drive their chariots with swift-skimming dolphins through the waves.

THE TREASURE CHEST

This frightful monster is come up out of the sea as a punishment to her vanity, and never will he retire till the guilty queen offer to him her dearest treasure, even An-drom'e-da, her daughter."

Throughout all the kingdom, then, was weeping and wailing, and most of all in the palace. Nevertheless, the people must at all costs be rid of the monster, so they seized the lovely Andromeda, bound her fast with chains to a mighty rock on the shore and left her a prey to the beast. Andromeda wrung her hands; the people stood afar off and watched, but they dared not let her free. Even Phin'e-us, whose promised bride she was, stood by and made no effort to save her. Pale and motionless as a marble statue, save for her hair that waved in the breeze, she stood.

Then lo! up out of the sea like a mountain he rose —the great sea-monster! Andromeda shrieked; the wretched mother and father wrung their hands; Phineus shrank back, slunk away, and hid himself in fear. But there in that moment of despair, borne

147

up in the air by his winged sandals, appeared the hero, Perseus.

"O virgin," he cried, "undeserving those chains. I am come to deliver you."

With a sudden swoop the youth darted down on the back of the monster, lighting just at the base of the neck where the creature could not strike at him with his fangs. Into his shoulder Perseus plunged his sword. Now here, now there, he worried him, piercing first this side, then that, and darting ever out of his reach by means of his wings. With a furious splashing the monster churned all the water about into foam. At length Perseus' wings were drenched. He dared no longer trust them. Alighting now on a rock and holding fast to a projecting fragment, as the monster floated near, he gave him his death blow. The serpent turned over on his back and floated with belly upward.

The people gathered on the shore raised a shout till all the hills re-echoed. The parents, transported with joy, called Perseus their deliverer, and the hero himself released Andromeda from the rocks. Then was the lovely Andromeda promised to Perseus in marriage. Every house in the city was wreathed and hung with garlands. In the palace itself a banquet was spread and all was joy and festivity.

But suddenly a noise was heard of warlike clamor. With a numerous party of swaggering, brawling followers, there burst into the festal hall, Phineus, demanding the maiden as his own. It was in vain that Cepheus cried: "You should have claimed her when she lay bound to the rock, the monster's victim. He who neglects his claim at such a time, forfeits it altogether."

Phineus made no reply, but hurled his javelin at Perseus. It missed its mark and fell harmless. Then the cowardly assailant ran and took shelter behind the altar. His act was the signal for a general onset by his band upon the guests of Cepheus. Perseus and his friends defended themselves and maintained for some time the unequal conflict, but the numbers of the assailants were far too great. Destruction seemed inevitable. Then with a loud voice Perseus cried: "If I have any friend here, let him turn away his eyes." And he suddenly held aloft the head of the gorgon, Medusa.

"Seek not to frighten us with your jugglery," cried one of the brawlers and raised his javelin to throw, but lo! he was turned to stone in the very act. A second was about to plunge his sword into a prostrate foe, but his arm stiffened and he could thrust not a hairsbreadth forward. A third, in the midst of a taunting boast, froze with mouth wide open. Phineus, beholding the dreadful result of his unjust aggression, felt confounded. He called aloud to his friends and got no answer. He touched them and found them stone. Then he fell on his knees before Perseus, to sue for his own wretched life, but in the very attitude he, too, was turned to stone.

Then was the marriage of Perseus and Andromeda fulfilled. King Cepheus gave Perseus a ship with stalwart rowers; he and his queen bade a fond farewell to their daughter, Andromeda, and Perseus and his bride set out for Seriphus.

Now it had happened that while Perseus had been away on his adventures, Polydectes had never once left off worrying Danae to force her to be his queen. His followers were as wicked as he, and in all the island was none to protect the lovely young matron, save Dictys, the good fisherman. At last, in his anger, the King cast Danae and Dictys both into dungeons, and there the two lay languishing when the ship of Perseus dropped anchor in the harbor.

Perseus made straight for the palace. The King was at meat surrounded by his wicked retainers. When he saw come into the hall the youth whom he had thought out of his way forever, he was sunk at first in confusion. In a moment more he cried out: "How dare you come here without the head of Medusa?"

"O King," Perseus answered, "I have the head in my pouch."

"Ho, ho!" mocked the King, "if you have in truth performed this unheard-of-act, then show us the head."

"Nay," answered Perseus. "I am loath to hold it up. I tell you I have it here in my pouch."

"Ho! ho!" jeered all the King's followers. "He has it in his pouch, yet he will not produce it! Base deceiver, he but pretends to have done the deed. It is no Medusa head he has in his pouch. He dares not show us what lies there."

"Come, come," called the King, "if you have there the head, out with it on the instant! Else with your own head you shall pay for the cheat."

Threatening, taunting, gibing, the King's men pressed about Perseus. "As you will, then," shouted the hero, and he held it aloft —the snaky head of Medusa. In a flash, about him were a white marble hall, a white marble table with white marble food and marble statues of men.

Having thus freed the island from the base tyranny of Poly-dectes, Perseus went to embrace his mother, set her free, and lead her to his Andromeda. Dictys likewise he freed and made King of Seriphus in place of his worthless brother. To Minerva, Perseus returned her shield along with the gift of the head of Medusa. To Mercury he gave back the sword. Then Perseus and Andromeda, with Danae, their mother, once more sailed away and after many adventures Perseus found a kingdom for himself. Long and wisely he reigned, and lived happily thenceforward.

The Labors of Hercules
A Greek Myth

WHEN Hercules was but a babe a few months old, his mother, Alc-me'ne, left him once asleep in a brazen warrior's shield that served him for a cradle. There came creeping upon him, while he slept, two venomous serpents. Just as the snakes were about to strike, Hercules awoke. With a crow of delight, as though he had found a new plaything and without a sign of fear, the little one seized the serpents, one in each hand. Straight by the neck he grasped them and held on tight. When his mother came in and found him thus, she was struck almost dumb at the sight, but the snakes were already strangled, and the infant Hercules safe. So began the strong man's conquests over evil.

Hercules grew to manhood possessed of marvelous courage and strength and carefully trained in all that befitted a hero. One day, when he was still a youth dwelling for a time among herdsmen on the mountains, he lay down in a lonely valley to sleep through the noonday heat. In his sleep he had a strange dream. He seemed to be following a path that suddenly split in two, branching off in opposite directions, and he knew not which road to take in order to pursue his journey. One road looked broad and easy and led down to a pleasant city whence he saw the

Once Hercules, in punishment for a wrong he had done, was sent to serve for three years as a slave at the court of Queen Omphale. Omphale forced the warrior to wear woman's clothes and spend his time spinning among her maidens while she swaggered about, dressed in his lion's skin, brandishing his club, and tyrannizing over him. This adventure of the hero is celebrated in music in the *Spinning Wheel of Omphale* by Saint-Saëns. The whirring of the spinning wheels is heard in the music, the high-pitched voices of maidens chiding Hercules for his awkwardness, the groans of the hero in his slavery, the queen's mocking laughter, and the whirring of wheels again.

gleam of marble palaces mid green and tempting gardens. The other was steep and rocky. It was hard to climb and led endlessly upward, growing rockier and rougher at every step, till it disappeared in the clouds. As Hercules stood hesitating which road to choose, there came dancing down the smooth and easy highway a gay and laughing maiden. She beckoned to him and called:

"Come with me, Hercules, down into the pleasant city. There you need not labor all day long in the heat of the sun. You may sit continually in fragrant gardens, hearken to the splash of fountains and the songs of birds, and slaves will serve you with all you need."

As Hercules looked toward the city, the piping of merry music faintly reached his ears to invite and tempt him still further. But lo! just then in the second path appeared a second young maiden, quite different from the first. She wore plain white garments and her eyes were grave, yet quiet, sweet and calm.

"My sister deceives you, Hercules," said she. "The pleasant things offered you down below are not worth the having. They are toys of which you will tire in a day and must be bought with a price of which you little dream. Do not descend thither, but climb the mountain path with me. You will find it rough and difficult, 'tis true. Yet, breasting its heights, you will there find real delights of which you can never tire. Moreover, if you have the courage to climb, this road will lead you to Mt. Olympus itself and there you shall live forever with the gods who cannot die."

And then in his dream Hercules turned his back on the gay and laughing maiden and took the mountain road. Thus did he choose the labors by means of which he turned his strength to good account for men.

Now Hercules had a cousin named Eu-rys'theus, King of My-ce'nae, who was a few days older than he. It had therefore been decreed that Hercules should be the slave of Eurystheus and in

The Youth of Hercules, by Saint-Saëns, shows Hercules choosing between pleasure and virtue. Muffled violins and wood-winds portray his indecision, alluring music invites to pleasure, but clarinet and oboe triumphantly declare his choice of virtue.

all things serve and obey him. Only on condition that he successfully performed twelve tasks that Eurystheus should set him, could he ever again be free. When Hercules presented himself at the court of King Eurystheus, he was already remarkable for his broad shoulders and the enormous muscles of his arms, while Eurystheus was miserably puny, timid, frail and weak. When Eurystheus for the first time beheld his powerful cousin, he was terrified at his strength, and he resolved to set him the hardest and most dangerous tasks that wit of man could possibly devise.

At this time in a beautiful grove that surrounded the temple of Ju'pi-ter in Ne-me'a, a fierce lion had its den. This lion was laying waste the whole countryside, so the people lived in constant terror of its ravages. The first task which Eurystheus set Hercules was to kill the Nemean lion. The young man set out with only his bow and arrows for weapons, but as he journeyed along he found a sturdy olive tree by the roadside. With a single wrench he pulled up the whole stout tree by its roots and made himself a club.

As he drew nearer the lion's haunts, nowhere did he meet with man, woman or child, for all had been so terrified that they kept within doors, leaving their flocks to its mercy. At length Hercules came to the beautiful grove by the Temple of Jupiter and there he watched all day long. Towards night the lion came creeping home to its lair. It was a tremendous creature, fierce and terrible. Hercules twanged his bow and sent an arrow flying. The arrow struck the beast, but so tough was its hide that the sharp point glanced aside and fell harmless. The lion snarled, showed its fierce teeth, and looked about for its foe. A second arrow Hercules shot, but it glanced aside like the first. Ere he could shoot a third, the lion had espied him. It crouched and sprang straight at his throat. Hercules knocked it aside with a powerful blow from his club, then as it rose ramping and clawing the air, he seized its neck with both hands and hung on fast till he slew it.

His first task thus accomplished, Hercules went back to Eurystheus, wearing the skin of the lion over his shoulder while the head of the beast rested on his own like a kind of helmet. Henceforth Hercules was always to be distinguished by the lion's skin which he wore and the enormous club which he carried. When he came in such fashion into Eurystheus' presence, the coward was as frightened as though he had suddenly seen the Nemean lion itself before him. Yet when he was somewhat calmed he said:

"Hercules has slain the Nemean lion, 'tis true, still, the lion was but a beast after all. I will send him now to dispose of a hideous monster."

So he sent for Hercules and bade him kill the powerful Ler'ne-an hydra. This hydra was a tremendous serpent with nine heads, one of which was immortal and could not possibly be slain. It had its den near a fountain that supplied all the region about with water and it drove the unfortunate peasants away, so they had no means whatever whereby to slake their thirst.

Hercules took with him his young nephew I'o-laus, and off they started. In an oozy, evil-smelling marsh they found the hydra, twisting its nine ugly heads in the air and breathing forth poison. Hercules made at it at once, but whenever he cut off a head, two grew in its place, so at every stroke it only became more formidable.

"Ho, Iolaus, set fire to yon grove of young trees," cried Hercules, "and keep me supplied with the burning brands."

Then he applied a brand to the neck wherever he cut off a head, and so prevented the new heads from growing. At length the immortal head alone was left. This Hercules had cleaved from the body, but it still spit its venomous poison as fiercely as before. So Hercules rolled a huge rock over it, and left it buried deep where it could never do further harm.

Now when Eurystheus found that his cousin had slain the hydra

as well as the lion, he began to
think there was no evil creature
that Hercules could not kill.

"But," he mused, "his third
task shall be harder still. After
all it is no great task to kill.
I shall bid him bring me *alive* the
fierce Er-y-man'thi-an boar."

Accordingly he gave orders,
and off went Hercules as before.
Straight to Mt. Erymanthus he
went and struggled long with
the famous wild boar, but he
caught him at length with his
naked hands and brought him
back on his shoulders. When
King Eurystheus saw Hercules
coming home with the boar
alive on his shoulders, he was
so badly frightened that he ran
and jumped into a great bronze

pot in one corner of his palace, pulling down the cover in haste
to keep himself well out of sight. He did not run so quickly
however, but that Hercules caught just a glimpse of him as the
cover went banging down.

"Ho, ho!" he cried out gravely, but with a twinkling eye, "this
pot is just the place in which to keep a boar that is like to tear
men to pieces." And he quickly lifted the lid and popped in the
boar on top of the King. Loud was the outcry, you may be sure,
till Hercules dragged out the two, the King in one hand, the boar
in the other, both kicking, struggling, roaring!

"His strength seems equal to any deed," said Eurystheus to

himself, "yet will I get the best of him this time by setting a task that demands not strength, but fleetness of foot, and superhuman endurance." Then he summoned Hercules to him and bade him bring him alive the stag of Di-an'a. This stag had often befooled the hunters of that region. It was most marvelously fleet of foot and few had ever seen it. But report had said it had horns of gold, and hoofs of brass. It could make the most wonderful leaps and was never wearied, no matter how long the dogs might have chased it. It had been seen browsing oftener than elsewhere close to the steps of Diana's Temple, and many people believed it was under the protection of that goddess.

So Hercules set out for the Temple of Diana, and watched and waited patiently. At last it appeared —the golden antlered creature, a sight of wondrous beauty. Every muscle a-quiver it stood, cautious and alert, ready to dart away at the slightest whisper of danger.

Hercules sprang towards it at once. It gave a mighty leap and made off, swift as the flying wind. But Hercules made after it, hot on its heels. Over hill, over dale it flew, through forest and meadow, over shallow stream and broad deep river, on and on and on. A whole year long it ran, over nearly the whole of Europe, and a whole year long Hercules followed, till at last he wearied it out and it fled back, exhausted and panting, to seek shelter in Diana's Temple. Even there Hercules would have seized it, but just then a flood of silver light shone gently round about, and there before him appeared a lovely lady in short white garments, with a bow and quiver at her back and a half moon on her crown. It was Diana herself, goddess of the moon and of the chase, and to her the stag ran trembling.

"You must not lay hands on this stag," she said. "It belongs to me. But return to King Eurystheus, and tell him how your endurance has wearied it out and how but for me you would have had it. I promise you he shall consider that your fourth labor is accomplished."

Now Eurystheus was almost at a loss how further to test such a Hercules, but he thought: "I have tried his strength, his endurance and agility. I will now try his wits and send him on an adventure that only the devising of some skillful plan can ever accomplish."

In the valley of Stym-pha'lus there had come an enormous flock of strange birds that did great damage to crops and herds, and even carried off children. These birds had claws of iron, and feathers of metal, sharp at the end, which they had the power of throwing down on their enemies. No fleetness of foot, endurance, or bodily strength could dispose of such foes as these, that could not be prevented from darting up into the air out of reach. So Eurystheus bade Hercules save the valley of Stymphalus from these ugly birds. Hercules wisely decided at once not to fight with such creatures. Instead, he went quietly into the deep dark wood where they had their nests by the side of a noisome pool. Holding his bronze shield above his head to protect himself from their feathers, he rang a great bell and at the same time beat on his shield with his lance. Frightened at this hideous noise the birds flew up in such numbers that they darkened all the sky. As they flew over Hercules' head, their feathers fell fast like hail on his shield, but he continued to ring the bell and beat the shield till every one of the birds had disappeared from the place, so frightened by the noise that none ever dared return.

Thereafter, Eurystheus set Hercules five well-nigh impossible labors more. First, he must clean out in one day the filthy stables of King Au-ge'as wherein the King had kept three thousand oxen for thirty years without ever cleansing their stalls. The refuse was piled mountain high, but Hercules dug a trench, turned the waters of two great rivers through the stables and cleaned them

thoroughly in one day. Then he must fetch to Mycenae alive the raging white bull of Crete, but he seized it by its horns and held it so firmly in spite of its terrible struggles that the bull saw it had met its master and followed him like a lamb. For his eighth labor he captured the savage man-eating horses of King Di-o-me′des; for the ninth he brought back the girdle of Hip-pol′y-ta, Queen of the Am′a-zons, a fierce tribe of war-like women who were never defeated in battle; for the tenth he overcame the giant Ger′y-on with his three great bodies, his three great heads, and six arms that waved like a windmill.

When Hercules always succeeded, his cousin was in despair. For his eleventh labor, Eurystheus set him what he deemed the most impossible task of all. He bade him never again show his face in Mycenae unless he brought back three golden apples from the Garden of the Hes-per′i-des, for he knew full well that no man on earth knew where to find that garden. But Hercules would not be daunted. He set out to westward where the sky glows golden at sunset. There, thought he, behind that golden gate should lie such a garden of golden fruit. He journeyed long and he journeyed far, but at last he came to a beautiful spot on the banks of a river, where a band of graceful river nymphs played hide and seek mid the rocks. As soon as they perceived the hero, they ran laughing, with ropes of flowers, to seize him and make him their prisoner. Then they led him into a shady beech grove, where they bade him sit on a grassy knoll and offered him refreshment of luscious purple grapes. But Hercules would not linger.

THE TREASURE CHEST

He begged the nymphs to tell him where lay the Garden of the Hesperides of which he was in search.

"You must seek out Pro'te-us, the Old Man of the Sea," they told him. "He knows every land whereon the ocean laps, but he will never tell you this secret unless you compel him. You must catch him and hold him fast no matter what may happen until he tells you the truth."

Thanking the nymphs for their kindness, Hercules again set out. He followed the river on and on till he heard the mighty boom of the sea. Then he advanced cautiously to the shore and there he saw fast asleep, lulled by the roar of the waters, a little old man whose hair and beard flowed down like a tangle of seaweed. Here, for certain, was the Old Man of the Sea himself and no doubt at all about it. So Hercules stepped forward, quickly

seized him by an arm and a leg, and held him fast.

"Tell me," he cried, "where lies the Garden of the Hesperides."

Proteus awoke in a fright, and the next instant Hercules found he was holding in his hands no little old man, but a struggling stag. The change was astounding enough but still Hercules held on tight. Then the stag became a sea bird screaming to be free, the sea bird changed to a fierce three-headed dog, the three-headed dog to a savage giant, the giant to a monstrous snake. But the more terrifying were the forms which the old man assumed, the tighter Hercules held him. At last perceiving that Hercules could not be frightened into letting him go, Proteus appeared in his own rightful form once more and told him the truth.

"Go down into Africa," he said, "where the giant At'las holds up the sky and Atlas will get the apples for you."

So Hercules set out for Africa, but he had scarcely touched the African shore, when he was attacked by the terrible giant, An-tae'us who let no man pass him alive. This giant was son of the earth, and the most difficult of all giants to conquer, for whenever he was knocked down he gained fresh strength from the dust and sprang up stronger than ever. But Hercules, knowing it was from the earth his strength had come, lifted him high above his head and held him there, struggling and kicking, separated from the source of his power, till the life was crushed out of him. Then he went again on his way.

Being wearied somewhat by the struggle, he soon lay down for a little rest and fell asleep. Suddenly he awoke, feeling as if he had been stung by a thousand insects. As he sat up and rubbed his eyes, what should he see about but a multitude of Pygmies —

tiny people, no larger than bumble bees, who had climbed up over his body and attacked him with their tiny bows and arrows. Another man might have been angered by their little teasing stings, but Hercules only laughed with a loud resounding guffaw, whereat the Pygmies all ran away, save a very few that Hercules caught in his hand, and tied up in a corner of his lion's skin to take back home to Eurystheus.

After this Hercules wandered on and on till he saw looming up before him —a mountain it looked to be, yet it was only a giant so tall that the clouds hung about his face like a beard and drifted around his shoulders. He was holding up his hands and on these and his head he bore the blue dome of the sky. At last, here was Atlas, and Hercules, nothing daunted by the fearful weight of the heavens under which even Atlas groaned, offered to relieve the giant by bearing the burden himself, if Atlas would get for him three golden apples from the Garden of the Hesperides. Atlas was more than willing, for the nymphs who guarded the apples were his nieces and to him the adventure was nothing more than a holiday. So Hercules climbed a mountain nearby to be of the giant's height, took the sky on his shoulders, and bore its tremendous weight while Atlas went off for the apples.

In due time back came the giant, but so much had he enjoyed his holiday, that he sought by a trick to give Hercules the slip and leave him forever with the sky on his shoulders. Hercules saw through the trick, however, outwitted the clumsy fellow, and made safely off with the apples.

Now that Hercules had accomplished eleven of the twelve labors, Eurystheus was beside himself. He could think of only

one task more that it seemed no man could ever achieve. He would send Hercules down into the underworld, the dark and gloomy abode of Plu'to, to bring thence the hideous three-headed watch-dog Cer'ber-us. Who that had entered those gloomy gates had ever been known to return? This would of a certain be the end of Hercules, for here, men said, was the abode of death.

Hercules journeyed away till he came to a deep chasm between two black and frowning rocks. Far, far below gleamed waters black as ink and now and again strange rumblings as of thunder shook the earth. Here was the only entrance to the underworld. Still Hercules knew no fear. Down into the deep black hole he climbed. There before him guarding the way, he saw Cerberus with his three savage heads and his tail like a snake. The dog let him enter readily. It would be when he sought again to go out that the creature would make at him.

Straight to Pluto's throne through the dark and dreary shadows went Hercules without once turning aside. Of Pluto himself he demanded permission to carry his watch-dog back to Mycenae. Pluto was struck with his daring.

"Hercules," said he, "you have done and suffered much, and proved yourself a true hero. Go, therefore. You shall take my watch-dog back if you can conquer him barehanded."

So Hercules returned once more to the gate. There stood Cerberus, no more quiet, but bristling with rage, showing his savage teeth, and crouching ready to spring. Hercules lost no time. He seized the dog on the spot with his vice-like grip, and dragged him straight off to Eurystheus.

When Eurystheus saw this remarkable sight, when he saw that Hercules had conquered even death and come back from that underworld whence men said none could ever return, he at once set his cousin free. At length the terms of his bondage had all been fulfilled. Nevertheless, Eurystheus strictly forbade Hercules ever again to enter the gates of Mycenae.

Thereafter, Hercules, now at last his own master, wandered over the earth ridding the world of many a monstrous evil and doing mighty deeds for the good of all mankind. When the end of his earth journey came, he laid himself down on a funeral pyre and bade men set it aflame. Bright purifying flames sprang leaping up about him. All that could ever die they burned away. Then the real Hercules, the immortal Hercules came out from the fire all shining and glorious. A rainbow appeared in the sky. Lo! it was Iris' bridge that led from earth to heaven. A moment after the clouds broke away; Iris in all her shimmering colors appeared and Mercury with his winged shoes. Over the rainbow bridge they led the immortal Hercules, as the maid of his dream had promised, to Mt. Olympus itself, there to live forever among the gods with all who are truly heroes.

Thor's Journey to Jo'tun-heim
A Norse Myth

WHEN the lightning leaps from cliff to cliff across the sky, and the thunder roars and rumbles, reverberating, rolling, crashing, then is the brazen chariot of Thor, the Thunderer, rolling and rattling over the heavens —thus said the Norsemen, sons of the Northland. From the hoofs of the goats that draw his chariot fly blazing sparks, about his head gleams a crown of burning flame. In his strong right hand he grips his red hot hammer, Mjol'ner, from whence spring thunderbolts. It is against the great frost giants who dwell in Jo'tun-heim that Thor makes war—the giants who send forth ice and snow and bitter winds to nip the tender buds and kill the flowers; who wrap the earth in wintry mists and ruin harvests by their tempests.

It happened once that the storm giants held the earth too long in bondage. Frozen lay the rivers, and frozen the earth till long past the time for the coming of swallows, and no man could till the ground or plant the tender seed. Then from far off Asgard where dwell the gods, came Thor, Thor, the friend of farmers, Thor, the Deliverer, to do battle with the giants.

At the close of day Thor and Lo'ki, his companion, came to a cottage on the edge of a wood. Then rapped Thor on the door with his iron gauntlet, and called those within to give them food and shelter. Shelter the poor people gladly gave but food they had not to offer. So Thor raised his hammer and slew his own goats to serve for their supper. Amazed stood the poor peasants before him, but thus spake Thor:

"Eat, eat what ye will! Only heed this command —break no single one of the bones, but cast them all when ye have finished into the skins on the floor."

Then Thor ate his fill, and Loki likewise, and the peasant, and his wife, and Thi-al'fi, their son, and Rosk'va, their daughter. But Thi-al'fi, the greedy one, secretly broke a bone, to come at the sweet, juicy marrow; then he cast the pieces onto the skin with the rest of the bones. Early on the morrow up rose Thor from his couch and over the goats' skins and bones flourished good Mjol'ner, his hammer. Lithe and light, lively and brisk, up sprang the goats, handsome and whole as before. Only one, alas! limped as he ran. Then Thor knew that some one had disobeyed him. Dark grew his brow as the storm cloud; he raised his powerful hammer and all stood about in terror.

"Some one has disobeyed me!"

On his knees fell Thi-al'fi before him confessing his fault, and such was his sorrow and terror that Thor relented and let his hammer fall harmless.

"Rise," he said, "but for thy fault thou and thy sister Rosk'va shall follow me henceforth and be my servants forever."

Then did Thor leave his chariot and his goats in the charge of the peasant, bidding him give them good care against his return, and he set off once more with Lo'ki, Thi-al'fi and Rosk'va on foot for the realm of the giants. All day through a bleak and desolate land they journeyed into a land of mist and fog and gloom. At nightfall they sought for a shelter. Before them out of the mist loomed dim outlines of a house. They entered a spacious doorway, broad and high. Within was no one, neither fire, nor light, nor food. Flinging themselves wearily on the floor, Thor and his companions fell asleep.

Not long had they slept when a strange trembling shook the earth and awoke them —a roar and long drawn rumbling.

"It is an earthquake!" cried Thi-al'fi. Thereat Thor sent Loki and the others for safety into an inner room that seemed to be one of five branching off from the outer hall, while he himself stood guard at the door. When day began to dawn, lo! he saw through the mist a tremendous giant lying near and he perceived that the

upheaval which they had thought an earthquake the night before was but the noise of his snoring! Boldly he approached the giant.

"Awake!" he cried, "and tell me who thou art."

"Who be I?" cried the giant, stretching and looking about. "Skry'mir, my little fellow —Skry'mir, the giant —that's who I be. But where hast thou taken my mitten?"

At that Thor perceived that the house wherein they had slept was naught but the giant's glove! He called his comrades to come forth and out they stepped from the thumb! Loudly guffawed the giant.

"Ho, ho! little ones!" laughed he. "Where do ye journey? Whither away so bold?"

When he heard they were traveling to Jo'tun-heim he offered to be their guide. All day long they journeyed and all day long did Skry'mir belittle them and make them believe themselves good-for-naught. At nightfall, ere he dropped off to sleep, he offered them whatever food they might wish to take from the great provision bag that hung on his shoulder. But when they tried to open the bag, not all four together, as Skry'mir had known full well, could unfasten the knots by which the giant had tied it. Then was Thor sorely wroth that Skry'mir should make them appear such weaklings, and he raised his hammer and dealt him a fearful blow on the forehead. The giant opened one sleepy eye.

"Was that a leaf fell on me?" said he.

A second time Thor lifted his hammer and hurled it with all his force at the head of the giant. But Skry'mir only murmured: "Methought an acorn dropped on my head."

Now Thor put forth such strength as never he knew he had, and smote the giant on the temple. "There must be birds overhead," said Skry'mir. "A feather just now tickled me."

Then did Thor go back to his comrades. Early on the morrow, Skry'mir pointed out the shortest road to Jo'tun-heim, and then took leave of his fellows. But first he said: "O Thor, I would give thee advice. Think not to stand up against the mighty ones

whom thou wilt find in Jo'tun-heim. Prepare to bow thyself rather before them, for I be the smallest among them!"

In spite of his words, on went Thor, and soon there before him and his comrades loomed up a glittering city of ice, with spires and pinnacles of icicles. So high it was that they had to bend back their heads to see its top. Slipping between the enormous bars of the gate, the travellers presented themselves in the great hall before Ut'gard-lo'ki, the King of the Giants about whom, on benches, sat his tremendous followers.

"Oho!" cried the King of the Giants, squinting contemptuously down as if at some little fly on the floor, which he could scarcely discover. "Whom have we here? Little Thor, as I live, out of Asgard. I have heard thou art small, but in truth I had never thought so small! 'Tis said thou hast strength, though, and can perform many great exploits! I scarce can believe it! Yet come, let us see what thou and thy comrades can do against my giants. Choose your own feat. At what will ye first contend?"

Then cried Lo'ki who had fasted long enough to feel great hunger: "In eating will I contend with any man among ye."

A great platter of meat the King ordered into the hall, and summoned his servant, Lo'gi, to contend with Lo'ki. Lo'ki sat himself at one end of the platter and Lo'gi at the other and both began to eat. Like an honest man an-hungered, ate Lo'ki, but when he was come to the center of the platter, there he met Lo'gi, and while Lo'ki had eaten but the meat, the giant had devoured meat and bones and platter as well!

"Not much can ye do at eating!" scornful, cried Ut'gard-lo'ki.

Then did Thor, nettled and keenly athirst, offer to outdo anyone at drinking. Immediately was brought a horn which the King declared strong men emptied at one draught, weaker men at two and the veriest weaklings at three. Eagerly Thor applied his lips to the rim. But though he drank long and deep, the water seemed not to grow less by so much as a hair's breadth. Again he tried and again. The horn remained ever full.

"Not much can ye do at drinking," scornful, cried Ut'gard-lo'ki.

Then cried Thi-al'fi that he would run a race with any among the giants. Came one named Hu'gi, and, though Thi-al'fi kept hot on his heels in three different races, Hu'gi ever outstripped him.

"Not much can ye do at running," scornful, cried Ut'gard-lo'ki.

Next shouted Thor that he would contend in lifting.

"Lift me then my house cat," cried the King. " 'Tis a trifling game at which we only exercise children. I should never propose it to Thor save that I have found him so puny a little stripling."

Angrily, Thor seized the cat. At first he could not budge her. Then he arched her back from the ground, then he lifted one mighty paw. The faces of the giants turned pale, still Ut'gard-lo'ki called, "Not much can ye do at lifting!"

Last of all, cried Thor in a fury: "Let me contend at wrestling."

"My poor old nurse, El'li, belike is a fit match for thee," jibed the King and into the hall came a feeble old hag, weak-seeming and bent nearly double. Yet she seized Thor in a grip like a vise. Valiantly he struggled, but the more he tightened his hold, the firmer stood El'li, till at last she had him on his knees. Then cried Ut'gard-lo'ki: "No more will we contend. In truth ye are good for naught!"

On the morrow at daybreak, Thor and his comrades, sad and heavy hearted, set out once more for home. Ut'gard-lo'ki accompanied them outside the gates of the city. Once there, he cried: "How now, Thor, hast thou met mightier men than thou? Is it so easy as thou didst think to conquer the giants?"

"Nay," Thor made honest answer, "I have come off badly. My heart sinks with shame that I have proved such a weakling!"

Then was the King struck with the blunt and open truth of him who never yet uttered untruth, and he cried:

"O Thor, of Asgard, thou goest hence from my kingdom —
forever and aye I trust, and now will I too speak the truth. Not
by superior force, as ye think have ye been defeated. It has all
been done by magic. All things have been made to seem to you
other than they were. Even have we made you think yourselves
weak and puny, when our very bones rattled for trembling and
fear of your strength. I myself am Skry′mir and any one of thy
mighty blows would have done for me, had I not in the mist,
which distorts all things out of their natural shape, made thee
believe a mountain my head. Not me didst thou strike but the
mountain. Lo′gi, against whom Lo′ki contended in eating, is wild-
fire, the devourer; Hu′gi, against whom Thi-al′fi ran, is thought,
and who can run faster than thought? The horn from which
thou, Thor, didst drink is connected with the ocean so thou

couldst never have drained it unless thou couldst drink dry the ocean. El'li, the wrestler, is old age, who throws so many strong men, and the cat thou couldst not lift is the Mid'gard serpent that encircles the world. Yet didst thou nearly outdo Lo'gi, Hu'gi and El'li and lift the Mid'gard serpent, and thou didst drink so much of the sea that on earth men thought the tide had gone out. By trickery only have we kept you from your triumph, but in trickery are we clever. If ye be wise come no more against us. With deception and illusion will we meet you always."

Then in his righteous wrath Thor lifted up his hammer. The might that was his, the power that was his, once more he knew. But as he swung good Mjol'ner, the giant vanished—vanished, too, the whole city of freezing ice and snow. Retreated had the giants before the power of Thor, perceived by them when to Thor himself his prowess had seemed so little. Fled had the giants before him. Then once more smiled the earth, free from the fetters of frost, ready for seed and bloom, and back to Asgard went Thor with Lo'ki, Thi-al'fi and Rosk'va.

THOR

HENRY WADSWORTH LONGFELLOW

I am the God Thor,
I am the War God,
I am the Thunderer!
Here in my Northland,
My fastness and fortress,
Reign I forever!

Here amid icebergs,
Rule I the nations;
This is my hammer,
Mjolner, the mighty;
Giants and sorcerers
Cannot withstand it!

—from The Saga of King Olaf.

The Stealing of I-du'na
A Norse Myth

IT happened once that O'din, the All-father, King of the gods, with Hoe'nir, his brother, and Lo'ki, the mischief-maker, started out of As'gard, the home of the gods, down across the Bridge of the Rainbow, to journey around the world. At eventide they came to a densely wooded mountain, and being anhungered, yet finding no dwelling in sight, they caught an ox from a herd that stood grazing near and dressed the meat for their supper. Then did Lo'ki, god of fire, kindle a flame to cook the food, but the time being come for the meat to be done, lo! it was raw as in the beginning. Another fire made Lo'ki, but all in vain. As raw was the meat as before. Then Lo'ki, O'din and Hoe'nir heard a noise in the branches above them. Looking up they perceived an eagle fanning the meat with his wings and sending a cold wind upon it that prevented it from roasting.

"Done to a turn will your meat be," croaked the eagle, "if you will promise me as much as I can eat."

"Nay, then!" cried the three out of Asgard. "Join us and eat what thou wilt."

So the eagle left off fanning the meat; it was soon cooked and they all went to help themselves. But the eagle, first of all, seized three-quarters of the whole ox. Then was Lo'ki angered. Seizing a stick lying near, he began to belabor the greedy bird. No sooner had he done so, than one end of the pole stuck fast in the eagle's feathers, and the other stuck fast to Loki's hands. Up flew the bird and off trailed Loki after him. Scraped through briery thickets and straggling branches of trees, jammed against rocks and stones, his arms nearly torn from their sockets, so was Loki dragged. Then he knew that the eagle was in truth no eagle, but Thi-as'si, the fierce frost giant. In vain he begged for mercy. The bird flew on the faster. Again and again he begged.

"On one condition only will I let thee go," croaked Thi-as'si,

All the freshness of spring is in *The Return of Spring* by Robert Schumann; the beautiful waltz, *Spring Voices*, by Johann Strauss; and "Spring Song," with its bird songs and rustling leaves from Victor Herbert's opera, *Natoma*.

"that thou lure out of Asgard the lovely I-du'na, and give her into my power with a dish of her magic apples, partaking of which keeps the dwellers in Asgard forever young."

At length Thi-as'si wrung from Loki the sorry promise to do as he bade him, and Loki was set free. Bedraggled and torn, back went Loki to Asgard.

Now I-du'na, Spirit of the Spring and of immortal youth, was loveliest of all the goddesses in Asgard. Tender green were her garments, on her head a wreath of flowers. Lightly she glided over the earth. At her approach the trees burst into bloom; myriads of flowers sprang up; tinkling brooks awoke and laughed and leapt for joy. Everywhere was stir, activity and life. Never was age where Iduna was, but always youth— eternal youth. And Iduna kept carefully guarded in her charge a tree that bore wonderful apples, which made him who ate them forever young. It was to partake of that eternal youth that the cruel frost giant wished to get possession of Iduna and her apples.

The husband of Iduna was Bra'gi, the god of poesy, who sings the wondrous song of life that scales the highest heavens and searches the depths of hell. Whenever he sings and plays on his golden harp, the flowers that spring up at Iduna's approach reveal their inmost charm and grace, the blending colors of earth and sky reveal their inmost harmony, the laughter of brooks, the songs of birds reveal their inmost joy; all nature finds a tongue and speaks and yields up the very secret of her being. To separate Iduna from Bragi was no easy task, but Loki waited until he saw the minstrel go forth on a journey from Asgard to earth, leaving Iduna unguarded. Then the mischief-maker went whither Iduna wandered alone in the midst of her flowery gardens.

"Iduna," said he, "just without the gates of Asgard I have found a tree that bears finer apples than thine. Sweeter to the taste are they and lovelier, and indeed I doubt not they restore youth and strength as well as thine."

"Nay, now," cried Iduna, "in all the world
are none such apples as mine."

"Come then with me and see," said Loki.
"And bring with thee a dish of thine own apples
that we may compare the two."

Into a crystal dish did Iduna then put her
precious apples and off with the wily Loki
went she. Scarcely were the two without the
safe protected gates of Asgard than Thiassi in his eagle plumage
swooped down upon Iduna. As the storm swoops, as the storm
rushes, when down from the mountain tops the wild north wind
comes roaring, so came Thiassi. From his frosty wings fell snow,
from his breath exhaled the cold that blasted all about. In his
talons seized he Iduna and bore her off to his wintry home in the
storm-bound land of Thrym'heim. There he shut her up in a
chamber in the rocks, against which all day long resounded the
boom and crash of the sea.

Each day he came and asked her to give him a bite of her
apples, for not unless Iduna herself gave out the precious fruit
would he who partook thereof find his youth and strength re-
newed. And every day Iduna stoutly refused. He whined and
begged and threatened—in vain! For no such creature of evil
was the gift of eternal youth. And when Thiassi himself thrust
his great fist in the dish to seize an apple, the fruit only dwindled
and shrunk till it disappeared altogether.

THE TREASURE CHEST

Long were the days, long were the months while Iduna stayed in Thrymheim. In Asgard, the heavens, and Midgard, the earth, spring and summer were gone. Cold winter held sway; leaves turned brown and fell; bird songs were hushed; flowers withered and drooped on their stalks; brooklets froze up into motionless silence, and all things seemed old and dying. In Asgard old age came stealing even upon the gods. Where, O, where was Iduna? Bragi mourned for her, Odin mourned for her, mourned all the dwellers in Asgard, mourned all the people of earth.

Then did Odin, the All-father, summon a council to consider what should be done. Thither all Asgard gathered—save Loki. Loki dared not appear. When Odin perceived that Loki alone was absent, he ordered Bragi to fetch him the maker-of-mischief. In the presence of Odin, before the might of his majesty, Loki was forced to pour out the tale of what he had done. Sternly Odin bade him go and bring back Iduna or never more dare show his face in Asgard.

So Loki borrowed of the goddess Frey'a her cloak of falcon feathers, and with this he was able to fly over land and sea to the rockbound coast of Thrymheim. Here in her gloomy cell he found the lovely Iduna. Thiassi, it chanced, was from home, so Loki forced his way through a narrow opening into her prison. Much she rejoiced to see him. He turned her at once into a swallow and flew off with her in his talons.

Not far had he gone, when he heard a rushing behind him. There in rapid pursuit was Thiassi. On and on flew Loki! On and on flew Thiassi, gaining little by little. On the walls of Asgard stood the gods wrinkled, and bent, and gray, watching far to southward over the sea, watching, longing for the coming of Iduna. At length they made out the falcon, Loki, and Thiassi hot on his heels. Long and anxiously watched they. Now Thiassi seemed pouncing on Loki's back, but always Loki escaped and flew with his precious burden on and on and on.

As he neared the city of refuge Loki's strength seemed almost failing. Then up rose the dwellers in Asgard and lit great fires on the walls that leapt and flamed to the heavens. Safe through the blaze and smoke dashed Loki —Loki the god of fire, but when Thiassi, creature of cold and storm, plunged blundering through, down he fell, suffocating, to his end beneath the mighty hammer of Thor. Then Loki let loose the swallow and up sprang the lovely Iduna herself, to be tenderly welcomed by Bragi, Odin and all the rest. And with Iduna and her apples, back to Asgard came youth and the joyous life of the Spring.

HOW THE GODDESS OF SPRING CAME TO SCORING

CHARLES KINGSLEY

White were the moorlands,
And frozen before her;
Green were the moorlands,
And blooming behind her.
Out of her gold locks
Shaking the spring flowers,
Out of her garments
Shaking the south wind,
Around in the birches,
Awaking the throstles,
And making chaste housewives all,
Long for their heroes home;
Loving and love-giving,
Came she to Scoring.
—from The Longbeard's Saga.

The Rose and the Ring*
WILLIAM MAKEPEACE THACKERAY

THIS is Valoroso XXIV—King of Paflagonia seated with his Queen and only daughter, Angelica, at their royal breakfast table—receiving the letter which announces to His Majesty a proposed visit from Prince Bulbo, heir of Padella, reigning King of Crim Tartary. Remark the delight upon the monarch's royal features. He is so absorbed in the letter, that he allows his eggs to get cold and leaves his august muffins untasted.

"What! That wicked, brave, delightful Prince Bulbo!" cries Princess Angelica.

"Who told you of him, my dear?" asks His Majesty.

"A little bird," says Angelica.

"Poor Giglio," says Mamma, pouring out the tea.

"Bother, Giglio!" cries Angelica tossing up her head which rustled with a thousand curlpapers.

"Angelica," says the King, "I hope you have plenty of new dresses. Your milliners' bills are long enough. My dear Queen,

*The *Rose and the Ring* was written by that great lover of fun, Thackeray, as a Christmas pantomime for children and illustrated with his own delightfully nonsensical pictures.

you must have some parties. And, my love, I should like you to have a new necklace. Order one. Not more than a hundred- or a hundred-and-fifty-thousand pounds."

"And Giglio, dear?" says the Queen.

"GIGLIO MAY GO TO THE . . . ."

"Oh, Sir!" screams Her Majesty. "Your own nephew! Our late King's only son."

"Giglio may go to the tailor's and order the bills to be sent in to Glumboso to pay. Confound him! I mean bless his dear heart. Give him a couple of guineas for pocket money, my dear; and you may as well order yourself bracelets while you are about the necklace, Mrs. V."

Her Majesty, or Mrs. V., as the King called her, embraced her husband; and, twining her arm round her daughter's waist, they quitted the breakfast room to make all things ready for the princely stranger.

When they were gone, the smile that lighted up the eyes of *husband* and *father* fled. He began to think to himself: "Why did I steal my nephew's, my young Giglio's . . . . Steal, said I? No, no, not steal! I took, and with my royal arm, I wield the sceptral rod of Paflagonia, and, on my manly head, I set the royal crown of Paflagonia. I took, and, in my outstretched hand, I hold the royal orb of Paflagonia. Could a boy, a sniveling, driveling boy—was in his nurse's arms but yesterday and cried for sugar-plums—bear up the awful weight of crown, orb, sceptre, and meet in fight the tough Crimean foe? The marriage of Angelica and Bulbo will unite two nations which have been engaged in bloody and expensive wars, the Paflagonians and the Crimeans. Were my brother, King Savio, alive, he would certainly will away the crown from his own son to bring about such a desirable union."

THE TREASURE CHEST

Thus easily do we deceive ourselves! Thus do we fancy what we wish is right! The King took courage, read the papers, finished his muffins and eggs, and rang the bell for his Prime Minister.

Now the truth of the matter was that when King Savio died, leaving his brother Valoroso as guardian of his infant son, the unfaithful guardian had himself proclaimed sovereign of Paflagonia under the title of King Valoroso XXIV. Prince Giglio, by reason of his tender age, did not feel the loss of his crown and empire. As long as he had plenty of toys and sweetmeats; a holiday five times a week; and, above all, the company of his darling cousin Angelica, the King's only daughter, Giglio was perfectly contented. Nor did he envy his uncle the great, hot, uncomfortable throne of state and the enormous, cumbersome crown in which the monarch appeared from morning till night.

No doubt the Queen must have been lovely in her youth, though she grew rather stout in after life. She was kind to her nephew; and, if she had any scruples about her husband's taking the young Prince's crown, she consoled herself by thinking that, at his death, Prince Giglio would be restored to his throne and share it with his cousin whom he loved so fondly.

The Prime Minister was Glumboso, an old statesman, in whose hands the monarch left all the affairs of his kingdom. All Valoroso wanted was plenty of money, plenty of hunting, plenty of flattery, and as little trouble as possible. He had statues erected to himself in every city of the empire. He was Valoroso the Magnanimous, Valoroso the Victorious, Valoroso the Great.

This royal pair had one only child, the Princess Angelica. It was said she had the longest hair, the largest eyes, the slimmest waist, the smallest foot, and the most lovely complexion of any young lady in the Paflagonian dominions. Her accomplishments were announced to be even superior to her beauty. She could play the most difficult pieces of music at sight. She knew every date in the history of Paflagonia, and every other country. She knew French, English, Italian, German, Spanish, Hebrew, Greek, Latin, Cappadocian, Samothracian, Aegean, and Crim Tartar. In a word, she was a most accomplished young creature, and her governess was Countess Gruffanuff.

Would you not fancy from this picture that Gruffanuff must have been a person of the highest birth? She looks so haughty that I should have thought her a princess at least. The fact is, she had been a maidservant to the Queen and her husband had been head footman. After his disappearance of which you shall hear more presently, this Mrs. Gruffanuff, by flattering and wheedling and toadying to her royal mistress, became a favorite with the Queen who gave her a title and made her governess to the Princess.

And now to tell you why the Princess had such a wonderful character for learning and accomplishments when she was as *idle as possible*, I must go back ever so far and tell you about the Fairy Blackstick. Between the kingdoms of Paflagonia and Crim Tartary, there lived a mysterious personage who was known as the Fairy Blackstick, from the ebony wand or crutch on which she rode to the moon sometimes, or upon other excursions of business or pleasure and with which she performed her wonders.

THE TREASURE CHEST

When she was young, she was always whizzing about from one kingdom to another upon her fairy blackstick conferring her fairy favors upon this Prince or that. She had turned numberless wicked people into beasts, birds, millstones, clocks, pumps, boot-jacks, umbrellas, or other absurd shapes. But after two- or three-thousand years of this sport, Blackstick grew tired of it. Or perhaps she thought: "What good am I doing by sending this Princess to sleep for a hundred years, or fixing a black pudding on to that booby's nose? I begin to think I do as much harm as good by my performances. There were my two young god-daughters, King Savio's wife and Duke Padella's wife. I gave them each a present to render them charming in the eyes of their husbands, but what good did my Rose and my Ring do to those two women? None on earth. From having all their whims in-dulged by their husbands, they became lazy, ill-humored, absurdly vain. They used actually to patronize *me*, the Fairy Blackstick, who could have turned them into baboons and all their diamonds into strings of onions by a single wave of my rod!"

So she locked up her books in her cupboard, and scarcely used her wand at all except as a cane to walk about with. The Queen of Paflagonia presented His Majesty with a son and heir, and guns were fired, the capital illuminated, and no end of feasts ordained to celebrate the young Prince's birth. It was thought the fairy, who was asked to be his godmother, would at least have presented him with an invisible jacket or a flying-horse; but, instead, Black-stick went up to the cradle of the child Giglio and said, "My poor child, the very best thing I can send you is a *little misfortune*." And this was all she would utter to the disgust of Giglio's parents, who died very soon after, when Giglio's uncle took the throne.

In like manner, when Cavolfiore, King of Crim Tartary, had a christening of his only child, Rosalba, the Fairy Blackstick was not more gracious. Whilst everybody was exclaiming over the beauty of the darling child, the Fairy Blackstick looked very sadly at the baby and its mother and said, "My good woman (for the Fairy was very familiar and no more minded a Queen than a washerwoman), my good woman, these people who are following you will be the first to turn against you; and, as for this little lady, the best thing I can wish her is a *little misfortune*." So she touched Rosalba with her black wand, looked severely at the courtiers, motioned the Queen an *adieu* with her hand, and sailed slowly up into the air out of the window.

When she was gone, the court people, who had been awed and silent in her presence, began to speak. "What an odious fairy she is—a pretty fairy, indeed!" they said. "Why, she went to the King of Paflagonia's christening and pretended to do all sorts of things for that family, and what has happened? Prince Giglio, her godson, has been turned off his throne by his uncle. Would we allow our sweet Princess to be deprived of her rights by any enemy? Never, never, never, never!"

And they all shouted in a chorus, "Never, never, never, never!"

Now how did these fine courtiers show their fidelity? The Duke of Padella (father of Prince Bulbo) rebelled against the King, who went out to chastise his rebellious subject. "Anyone rebel against our beloved and august monarch!" cried the courtiers. "Anyone resist him? Pooh! He is invincible, irresistible! He will bring home Padella a prisoner and tie him to a donkey's tail!" The King went forth to vanquish Padella and the poor Queen, who was a very timid, anxious creature, grew so frightened and ill that she died, leaving injunctions with her ladies to take care of the dear little Rosalba. Of course, they said they would. Of course, they vowed they would die rather than any harm should happen to the Princess. At first the *Crim Tartar Court Journal* stated that the King was obtaining great victories over the audacious rebel; the troops of the infamous Padella were in flight—then the news came that King Cavolfiore was vanquished and slain by His Majesty, King Padella, the First!

THE TREASURE CHEST

At this news, half the courtiers ran to pay their duty to the conquering chief; and the other half ran away, laying hands on all the best articles in the palace. Poor little Rosalba was left there quite alone. She toddled from one room to another, crying, "Countess! Duchess!" (Only she said, "Tountess, Duttess," not being able to speak plainly.) "Bring me my mutton sop; my Royal Highness hungy!" She went from the private apartments into  the throne room, and nobody was there; and thence into the ballroom, and nobody was there; she toddled down the great staircase into the hall, and nobody was there. As the door was open, she went into the garden and thence into the forest where the wild beasts live and was never heard of any more. A piece of her torn mantle and one of her shoes were found in the wood in the mouths of two lionesses' cubs whom King Padella and a royal hunting-party shot. "So the poor little Princess is done for," said he. "Well, what's done can't be helped. Gentlemen, let us go to luncheon!" And one of the courtiers took up the shoe and put it in his pocket. And there was an end of Rosalba!

When the Princess Angelica was born, her parents not only did not ask the Fairy Blackstick to the christening party, but gave orders to their porter absolutely to refuse her if she called. This porter's name was Gruffanuff and he had been selected for the post because he was a very tall, fierce man, who could say "Not at home," to an unwelcome visitor with a rudeness which frightened most such persons away. He was the husband of Countess Gruffanuff, and they quarreled from morning till night.

Now this fellow tried his rudeness once too often; for when the Fairy Blackstick came to call on the Prince and Princess who were actually sitting at the open drawing-room window, Gruffanuff not only said they were not at home, but he made the most *odious, vulgar sign.* "Git away, h'old Blackstick," said he. "I tell you, Master and Missis ain't at home to you." He was going to slam the door, when the Fairy with her wand prevented the door being shut. Gruffanuff came out again in a fury and asked the Fairy "whether she thought he was a-going to stay at that there door all day?"

"You *are* going to stay at that door all day and all night and for many a long year," said the Fairy, very majestically.

"Ha, ha, that *is* a good un," cried Gruffanuff. "Ha-ah-what's this? Let me down!" For, as the Fairy waved her wand, he felt himself rising off the ground and fluttering up against the door. A screw ran into his stomach, and he was pinned to the door. His arms flew up over his head and his legs twisted under his body. He felt cold, cold growing over him, as if he was turning into

RING ALSO

metal; and he said, "O–o–H'm" and could say no more because he was dumb. He was neither more nor less than a knocker, a brass knocker! And there he was, nailed to the door in the blazing summer day till he burned almost red-hot. And there he was nailed to the door all the bitter winter nights till his brass nose was dropping with icicles. And the postman came and rapped at him and the vulgarest boy with a letter came and hit him up against the door and the housemaid came and scrubbed his nose with sandpaper. He had plenty of leisure now to repent of having been rude to the Fairy Blackstick. As for his wife, she did not miss him. As he was always guzzling beer, notoriously quarreling, and in debt to tradesmen, it was supposed he had run away to Australia or America.

Now one day, when the Princess Angelica was quite a little girl, she was walking in the garden of the palace with Mrs. Gruffanuff holding a parasol over her head to keep her complexion from the freckles. Angelica was carrying a bun to feed the swans and ducks in the royal pond, when there came toddling up to them such a funny little girl! She had a great quantity of hair blowing about her chubby little cheeks and looked as if she had not been washed or combed for ever so long. She wore a ragged bit of a cloak and had only one shoe on.

"You little wretch, who let you in here?" asked Gruffanuff.

"Div me dat bun," said the little girl, "me vely hungry."

"Hungry! What is that?" asked Princess Angelica and gave the child the bun.

"O Princess," said Gruffanuff, "how good, how kind you are. See, Your Majesties," she said to the King and Queen who now came up with Prince Giglio, "how kind the Princess is."

"I didn't want the bun," said Angelica.

"You're a darling little angel just the same," said the governess.

"Yes, I know I am," said Angelica. "Dirty little girl, don't you think I am very pretty?"

"O pooty, pooty!" said the little girl, capering about, laughing and dancing and munching her bun. And as she ate she began to sing:

"Oh what fun to have a plum bun!
How I wis it never was done!"

Angelica, Giglio, and the King and Queen began to laugh very merrily.

"I can dance as well as sing," said the little girl.

"I can dance, and I can sing,
And I can do all sorts of ting."

And she ran to a flower bed, made herself a wreath, and danced before the King and Queen so drolly and prettily that everybody was delighted.

"Who was your mother? Who were your relations?" said the Queen.

The little girl said:

"Little lion was my brudder,
Great big lioness was my mudder;
Neber heard of any udder!"

And she capered away on her one shoe, and everybody was exceedingly diverted. So Angelica said to the Queen, "Mamma, my

parrot flew away yesterday and I don't care any more for my
toys; and I think this funny little child will amuse me. I will
take her home and give her some of my old frocks, which I have
worn ever so many times and am quite tired of."

"Oh, the generous darling!" said Gruffanuff.

The child clapped hands and said,

> *"Go home with you—yes!*
> *You pooty Princess!*
> *Have a nice dinner, and wear a new dress!"*

And they all laughed again and took the child home to the
palace where, when she was washed and combed and had one of
the Princess's frocks given her, she looked as handsome as Angelica,
almost. In order that the little girl should not become too proud
and conceited, Mrs. Gruffanuff took her old, ragged mantle and
one shoe and put them into a glass box with a card laid upon
them, upon which was written, "These were the old clothes in which
little Betsinda was found when the great goodness and admirable

kindness of her Royal Highness, the Princess Angelica, received this little outcast."

For a while, little Betsinda was a great favorite with the Princess, but when the Princess got a monkey and afterwards a little dog and afterwards a doll, she did not care for Betsinda any more. Betsinda became very melancholy and quiet and sang no more funny songs because nobody cared to hear her. Then, as she grew older, she was made a lady's maid to the Princess. She worked and mended and put Angelica's hair in papers and was never cross when scolded. Whilst the Princess was having her masters in music, drawing, dancing, and languages, Betsinda would sit and watch; and, in this way, she picked up a great deal of learning for she was always awake though her mistress was not. When the Princess was going out, she would say: "My good Betsinda, you may as well finish what I have begun."

"Yes, miss," Betsinda would say and sit down very cheerfully, not to *finish* what Angelica began, but to *do* it! And Angelica actually believed that she did these things herself and received all the flattery of the court, as if every word of it was true.

And now let us speak about Prince Giglio, the nephew of the King. The young Prince was very good-natured and did not care for the loss of his crown, being a thoughtless youth not much inclined to politics or any kind of learning. On the other hand, the King's gamekeepers and huntsmen found the Prince an apt pupil. The First Lord of the Billiard Table gave the most flattering reports of the Prince's skill; so did the groom of the Tennis Court; and, as for the Captain of the Guard and Fencing Master, the valiant Count Kutasoff Hedzoff, he vowed he never had encountered so expert a swordsman as Prince Giglio.

THE TREASURE CHEST

Her Majesty, the Queen, always wished that Angelica and Giglio would marry; so did Giglio; so did Angelica, sometimes; but then, you know, she was so clever and Giglio knew nothing. When they looked at the stars, what did Giglio know of the heavenly bodies. He had never even heard of the Constellation of  the Bear. Once, when on a sweet night in a balcony where they were standing, Angelica said, "There is the Bear."

"Where?" said Giglio. "Don't be afraid, Angelica! If a dozen bears come, I will kill them rather than they shall hurt you."

"Oh, you silly," said she, "you are good, but not very wise."

"When Prince Giglio marries the Princess and comes to the throne, we, who have always been unkind to him, shall lose our places in a trice," thought Gruffanuff and Glumboso, the Prime Minister of Paflagonia. So these unprincipled people invented a hundred cruel stories about poor Giglio in order to influence the King, Queen, and Princess against him; how he was so ignorant that he could not spell the commonest words; how he owed ever so much money to the pastry cooks; how he used to go to sleep in church. All this backbiting had affect on Princess Angelica, who began to look coldly on her cousin, then to laugh at him; and, at Court balls, to treat him so unkindly that poor Giglio became quite ill, took to his bed, and sent for a doctor. Whilst he was lying sick, there came to the Court a painter whose name was

Tomaso Lorenzo and he was Painter in Ordinary to the King of Crim Tartary. One day Lorenzo showed the Princess a portrait of a young man in armor, with fair hair and the loveliest blue eyes.

"Dear Signor Lorenzo, who is that?" asked the Princess.

"I never saw anyone so handsome," says Gruffanuff (the old humbug).

"That," said the Painter, "that, madame, is the portrait of my august young master, His Royal Highness Bulbo, Crown Prince of Crim Tartary, and Knight Grand Cross of the Order of the Pumpkin. That is the Order of the Pumpkin glittering on his manly breast and received from King Padella I, for gallantry at the battle of Rimbombamento, when he slew two-hundred-and-eleven giants."

"What a prince!" thought Angelica, "so brave, so young!"

"He is as accomplished as he is brave," continued the Painter. "He knows all languages, composes operas and danced in a ballet in which he looked so beautiful that his cousin, the lovely daughter of the King of Circassia, died for love of him."

"Why did he not marry the poor princess?" sighed Angelica.

"The Prince has given his heart *elsewhere*," said the Painter.

"And to whom?" asked Her Royal Highness.

"I am not at liberty to mention the Princess's name!"

"Does it begin with a Z?" asked Angelica.

The Painter said it wasn't a Z, then she tried a Y and went backwards through the alphabet. Then she came to B, *and it wasn't* B! "Oh, dearest Gruffanuff," she said, "lend me your smelling bottle." And, hiding her head on the Countess's shoulder, she faintly whispered, "Ah, Signor, can it be A?"

THE TREASURE CHEST

It was A! "And though I may not tell Your Royal Highness the Princess's name, whom he fondly, madly, devotedly, rapturously loves, I may show you her portrait," said this slyboots. And leading the Princess up to a gilt frame, he drew back a curtain. Goodness! The frame contained a LOOKING GLASS, and Angelica saw her own face!

In the meanwhile, poor Giglio lay upstairs in his chamber very sick. The only person who visited him was little Betsinda, the housemaid, who used to bring him his gruel and warm his bed. When the little housemaid visited him morning and evening, Prince Giglio used to say, "Betsinda, has the Princess Angelica asked for me today?"

And Betsinda would answer, "No, my Lord, not today." But she was such a good-natured creature that she brought him up roast chicken and jellies from the kitchen, saying that the Princess had made the jelly or the bread sauce with her own hands on purpose for Giglio.

When Giglio heard this, he took heart and began to mend immediately. He felt so much better the next day that he dressed and went downstairs, where whom should he meet but Angelica going into the drawing-room? All the covers were off the chairs, the chandeliers taken out of the bags, and the damask curtains uncovered. Angelica had her hair in curlpapers. In a word, it was evident there was going to be a party.

"Heavens, Giglio!" cried Angelica, "*you* here in such a dress!"

"Yes, dear Angelica, I am come downstairs today thanks to the *fowl* and the *jelly*."

"What do I know about fowls and jellies?" said Angelica.

"Why, didn't—didn't you send them, Angelica dear?" said Giglio.

"I send them! Angelica dear! No, Giglio dear," said she, mocking him. "I was engaged getting the rooms ready for His Royal Highness, the Prince of Crim Tartary, who is coming to pay my papa a visit."

"The–Prince–of–Crim–Tartary!" Giglio said, aghast.

"Yes, the Prince of Crim Tartary," said Angelica. "I dare say you never heard of such a country. What *did* you ever hear of? You are so ignorant you are not fit for society! Go and put your best clothes on to receive the Prince, and let me get the drawing-room ready."

Giglio said, "Oh, Angelica, Angelica, I didn't think this of you. *This* wasn't your language to me when you gave me this ring, and I gave you mine in the garden and gave me that k. . ."

But Angelica in a rage cried, "Get out, you saucy, rude creature! How dare you to remind me of your rudeness? As for your little trumpery, two-penny ring, there, sir, there!" And she flung it out of the window.

"It was my mother's marriage ring," cried Giglio.

"I don't care whose marriage ring it was," cried Angelica. "Marry the person who picks it up! You shan't marry me!"

Now Angelica little knew that the ring which Giglio had given her was the fairy ring which Blackstick had given to Giglio's mother. If a man wore it, it made all the women love him. If a woman, all the gentlemen. The Queen, Giglio's mother, was admired immensely whilst she wore this ring; but, when she called little Giglio and put the ring on his finger, everyone's love was transferred to him. And when, as quite a child, Giglio gave it to Angelica, people began to love *her*.

"Yes," said Angelica in her foolish, ungrateful way, "I know who'll give me much finer things than your beggarly little pearl nonsense!"

"Very good, miss! You may take back your ring, too!" said Giglio. And, then, as if his eyes had been suddenly opened, he cried, "Is this the woman I have been in love with all my life? Why . . . actually . . . yes . . . you are a little crooked!"

"Oh, you wretch!" cried Angelica.

"And, upon my conscience, you squint a little!"

THE TREASURE CHEST

"You brute! You brute, you!" Angelica screamed out, when, with a low bow, the first lord-in-waiting entered and said: "Royal Highnesses! Their Majesties expect you in the Pink Throne Room where they await the arrival of the Prince of CRIM TARTARY."

Prince Bulbo's arrival had set all the Court in a flutter. Everybody was ordered to put on his or her best clothes; the footmen had their gala liveries; the Lord Chancellor his new wig; and Countess Gruffanuff, you may be sure, was glad of an opportunity to decorate *her* old person with her finest things. She was walking through the court on her way to wait upon their Majesties when she spied something glittering on the pavement and bade the boy in buttons, who was holding up her train, go and pick it up. It was a trumpery, little ring, too small for her old knuckles, so she put it in her pocket. "Oh, mum!" said the boy, looking at her, "how—how beyoutiful you do look, mum, today, mum!"

The guards saluted her with peculiar respect. Captain Hedzoff said, "My dear madam, you look like an angel today." And so, bowing and smirking, Gruffanuff went in and took her place behind her Royal Master and Mistress. Princess Angelica sat at their feet, and behind the King's chair, stood Prince Giglio looking very savage.

The Prince of Crim Tartary made his appearance, attended by Baron Sleibootz, his chamberlain, and followed by a black page carrying the most beautiful crown. He was dressed in his travelling costume, and his hair, as you see, was a little in disorder.

"I have ridden three-hundred miles since breakfast," said he, "so eager was I to behold the Prin—, the Court and august family of Paflagonia, and I could not wait one minute before appearing in your Majesties' presences."

Giglio burst out with a roar of contemptuous laughter.

"Your Highness is welcome in any dress," said the King.

"Any dress His Royal Highness wears *is* a Court dress," said Princess Angelica, smiling graciously.

"Ah! but you should see my other clothes," said the Prince. "I should have had them on, but that stupid carrier has not brought them. Who's that laughing?"

It was Giglio laughing. "I was laughing," he said, "because you said just now that you were in such a hurry to see the Princess, you could not wait to change your dress; and now you say you come in those clothes because you have no others."

"And who are you?" said Prince Bulbo very fiercely.

"My father was King of this country, and I am his only son," replied Giglio, with equal haughtiness.

"Ha!" said the King and Glumboso looking very flurried, but the King, collecting himself, said, "Dear Prince Bulbo, I forgot to introduce to Your Royal Highness my dear nephew, His Royal Highness, Prince Giglio! Giglio, give His Royal Highness your hand!" and Giglio, giving his hand, squeezed poor Bulbo's until the tears ran out of his eyes. Glumboso now brought a chair for the royal visitor; but he placed it on the edge of the platform on which the King, Queen, and Princess were seated. As Bulbo sat down, it toppled over, and he with it, rolling over and over and bellowing like a bull.

Giglio roared still louder at this disaster and so did all the Court; for, as Bulbo stood up from his fall, he looked so exceedingly plain and foolish that nobody could help laughing. When he had entered the room, he was observed to carry a rose in his hand which fell out of it when he tumbled.

"My rose! My rose!" cried Bulbo. And his chamberlain picked it up and gave it to the Prince, who put it in his waistcoat. Then people wondered why they had laughed; there was nothing particularly ridiculous about him. So they sat and talked, the royal personages together—Giglio very comfortable with Gruffanuff behind the throne. He looked at her with such tender eyes, that her heart was all in a flutter. "Oh, dear Prince," she said, "how could you speak so haughtily in presence of their Majesties? I thought I should have fainted."

"I should have caught you in my arms," said Giglio, looking raptures.

"Why were you so cruel to Prince Bulbo, dear Prince?" said Gruffanuff.

"Because I hate him," replied Giglio.

"You are jealous of him and still love poor Angelica," cried Gruffanuff, putting her handkerchief to her eyes.

"I did, but I love her no more!" Giglio cried.

"What are you two people chattering about there?" said the Queen. "It is time to dress for dinner."

When Prince Bulbo got to his room, he found his luggage there and unpacked; and the hairdresser cut and curled him. When

the dinner bell rang, the royal company had not to wait above five-and-twenty minutes until Prince Bulbo appeared. As for Giglio, he never left Madame Gruffanuff all this time, but stood with her in a window paying her compliments. At length, the groom of the Chambers announced His Royal Highness, the Prince of Crim Tartary.

THE TREASURE CHEST

The noble company went into the royal dining-room. You may be sure they had a very good dinner, after which, His Majesty and the Queen went to sleep in their armchairs.

Bulbo went and sat by the piano where Angelica was playing and singing, and he sang out of tune and upset the coffee and talked absurdly and fell asleep and snored horribly. But Angelica still persisted in thinking him the most beautiful of human beings. No doubt the magic rose, which Bulbo wore, caused this infatuation on Angelica's part. Giglio must go and sit by Gruffanuff whose old face he, every moment, began to find more lovely. He paid the most outrageous compliments to her: There never was such a darling! Older than he? Fiddle-de-de! He would marry her—he would have no one but her!

Marry the heir to the throne! Here was a chance! The artful hussy got a sheet of paper and wrote upon it: "This is to give notice that I, Giglio, son of Savio, King of Paflagonia, hereby promise to marry the charming and virtuous Barbara Griselda, Countess Gruffanuff, and widow of the late Jenkins Gruffanuff, Esq."

"What is it you are writing, you charming Gruffy?" said Giglio.

"Only an order for you to sign, dear Prince, for giving coals and blankets to the poor this cold weather. Look! The King and Queen are both asleep and your Royal Highness's order will do." So Giglio, who was very good-natured as Gruffy well knew, signed the order immediately; and, when she had it in her pocket, what airs she gave herself. She was ready to flounce out of the room before the Queen as now she was the wife of the *rightful* King of Paflagonia! And when candles came and she had helped undress the Queen and Princess, she went to her room, she practiced writing her own name with all the titles of a Queen.

Little Betsinda came to put Gruffanuff's hair in curlpapers and the Countess was so pleased, that, for a wonder, she complimented Betsinda. "Betsinda!" she said, "you dressed my hair very nicely today. I promised you a present. Here is a

pretty little ring that I picked—that I have had some time."
And she gave Betsinda the ring she had picked up in the court.

"It's like the ring the Princess used to wear," said the maid.

"No such thing," said Gruffanuff, "I have had this ever so long. There, tuck me up quite comfortable; and, as it's a very cold night, you may go and warm dear Prince Giglio's bed."

"I had best warm both the young gentlemen's beds," said Betsinda. Gruffanuff, for reply, said, "Hau–au–ho! Grau–haw–hoo! Hong–hoho!" In fact she was snoring, sound asleep.

Betsinda went first to Prince Giglio's bed with her warming pan, then to Prince Bulbo's room. Prince Bulbo came in and as soon as he saw her he cried: "Oh! Oh! Oh! Oh! Oh! Oh! What a beyou–oo–ootiful creature you are! You angel—you pearl—you rosebud! Fly to the desert with me! Be mine! Be mine! Be mine!"

"Go away, please, Your Royal Highness," said Betsinda.

But Bulbo said:

> *"No, never till thou swearest to be mine.*
> *Thou lovely blushing chambermaid, divine!*
> *Here at thy feet the royal Bulbo lies,*
> *The trembling captive of Betsinda's eyes."*

And he went on, making himself so *absurd and ridiculous* that Betsinda, who was full of fun, gave him a touch with the warming pan. That made him cry "Oh–o–o–o" in a very different manner.

Prince Bulbo made such a noise that Prince Giglio, who

heard him, came in to
see what was the
matter. As soon as he
saw what was taking
place, Giglio, in a fury,
rushed on Bulbo, kick-
ing him till his hair was
quite out of curl. Poor
Betsinda did not know
whether to laugh or
cry. And, when Giglio
had done knocking
Bulbo about, what do
you think Giglio does?
He goes down on his
knees to Betsinda,
takes her hand, begs
her to accept his heart

and offers to marry her that moment. Fancy Betsinda's condition, who had been in love with the Prince ever since she first
saw him in the palace garden when she was quite a little child.

"O divine Betsinda," says the Prince, "how have I lived fifteen
years in thy company without seeing thy perfections? Angelica?
Pish! Gruffanuff? Phoo! The Queen? Ha, ha! Thou art my queen!"

"O Prince, I am but a poor chambermaid," says Betsinda.

"Didst thou not tend me in my sickness when all forsook me?"
continues Giglio. "Did not thy gentle hand smooth my pillow
and bring me jelly and chicken?"

"And I sewed Your Royal Highness's shirt buttons on, too,
if it please Your Royal Highness," cries this artless maiden.

When Prince Bulbo, now madly in love with Betsinda saw the
unmistakable glances which Betsinda flung upon Giglio, he began
to cry bitterly and tore quantities of hair out of his head.

And, as the princes now began to quarrel and be very fierce with one another, Betsinda thought proper to run away.

"You great, big, blubbering booby," cried Giglio, "you dare to kneel down at Princess Giglio's knees and kiss her feet!"

"She's not Princess Giglio," roars out Bulbo. "She shall be Princess Bulbo! No other shall be Princess Bulbo."

"I'll have your life," cries Giglio.

"I'll run you through," cries Bulbo.

"I'll cut your throat."

"I'll blow your brains out."

"I'll knock your head off."

"We'll meet again," says Giglio, shaking his fist in Bulbo's face; and, seizing up the warming pan, he rushed downstairs. What should he see on the landing but His Majesty talking to Betsinda. His Majesty had heard the row in the building and, smelling something burning, had come out to see what the matter was.

"It's the young gentlemen smoking, perhaps, Sir," says Betsinda.

"Charming chambermaid," said the King, "never mind the young men! Turn thine eyes on a middle-aged autocrat who has been considered not ill-looking in his time."

"Oh, Sir! what will Her Majesty say?" cries Betsinda.

"Her Majesty!" laughs the monarch. "Her Majesty be hanged! Runs not a river by my palace wall? Have I not sacks to sew up wives withal? Say but the word and thou wilt be mine own — your mistress straightway in a sack is sewn, and thou the sharer of my heart and throne!"

THE TREASURE CHEST

When Giglio heard these atrocious sentiments, he forgot the respect usually paid to Royalty. He lifted up the warming pan and knocked the King flat as a pancake, after which Master Giglio took to his heels and ran away. Betsinda went off screaming; and the Queen, Gruffanuff, and the Princess, all came out of their rooms. Fancy their feelings on beholding their husband, father, sovereign, in this posture! As soon as the coals began to burn him, the King came to himself and stood up.

O piteous spectacle! the King's nose was bent quite crooked by the blow of Prince Giglio! His Majesty ground his teeth with rage. "Ho! my Captain of the Guard!" he cried. "Hedzoff, seize the Prince! But now he dared, with sacrilegious hand, to strike the sacred nightcap of a king and floor me with a warming pan! The villain dies! See it be done!" And lifting up the tails of his dressing-gown, the King entered his own room, followed by the Queen and the Princess.

Captain Hedzoff was very much affected, having a sincere love for Giglio. "Poor, poor Giglio!" he said, the tears rolling over his manly face. "My noble young Prince, is it my hand must lead thee to death?"

"Lead him to fiddlestick, Hedzoff," said a female voice. It was Gruffanuff. "The King said you were to hang the Prince; well, hang the Prince!"

"I don't understand," said Hedzoff, who was not a very clever man.

"You Gaby! He didn't say *which* Prince," said Gruffanuff. "Well, then, take Bulbo and hang *him*."

When Captain Hedzoff heard this, he began to dance for joy.

"Prince Bulbo's head will do capitally," he said and he went to arrest the Prince the very first thing next morning.

"Pooh, pooh, my good man! Stop, I say!" was all the luckless Bulbo could say, for Hedzoff's guards, seizing him, tied a handkerchief over his mouth and carried him to the place of execution.

Gruffanuff got up early next morning to devise some plan for rescuing her darling husband, as the silly, old thing insisted on calling Giglio. She found him walking in the garden thinking up a rhyme for Betsinda—having, indeed, forgotten all about the past evening.

"Well, dear Giglio," says Gruffanuff.

"Well, dear Gruffy," says Giglio, only *he* was satirical.

"I have been thinking, darling, what you must do in this scrape. You must fly the country for awhile."

"Fly the country? Never without her I love!" says Giglio.

"No, she will accompany you, dear Prince," she says in her most coaxing accents. "First, we must get the jewels of the King and Queen. Here is the key, duck. They are all yours by right, you know! And having got the jewels, go to Glumboso's apartment where, under his bed, you will find sacks containing money which he took from your royal father's room on the day of his death. With this we will fly."

"*We* will fly?" said Giglio.

"Yes, you and your bride—your Gruffy!" says the Countess with a languishing leer.

"*You* my bride!" says Giglio. "You, you hideous old woman!"

"Oh, you wretch! Didn't you give me this paper promising marriage?" cries Gruffanuff.

"Get away, you old goose! I love Betsinda and Betsinda only!" And, in a fit of terror, Giglio ran from her as quickly as he could.

"He! he! he!" shrieks out Gruffanuff, "a promise is a promise if there are laws in Paflagonia! And as for that vixen, Betsinda, Master Giglio may look long before finding *her*, I warrant."

Alas and woe is me! Very lamentable events had occurred to Betsinda that morning. The King had offered to marry her. Of course, Her Majesty, the Queen, was jealous! Bulbo had fallen in love with her. Of course, Angelica was furious! Giglio was in love with her; and oh, what a fury Gruffy was in!

"Take off that cap I gave you! Take off that petticoat I gave you! Take off that gown I gave you!" they said all at once and began tearing the clothes off poor Betsinda.

"Give her the rags she wore when she came to the house, and turn her out!" cried the Queen.

Taking up the Queen's poker, the cruel Gruffanuff drove Betsinda into her room. The Countess went to the glass box in which she had kept Betsinda's old cloak and shoe this ever so long and said: "Take those rags, you little beggar creature and strip off everything belonging to honest people and go about your business!" And she actually tore off the poor little delicate thing's back almost all her clothes.

Poor Betsinda huddled the cloak round her on which were embroidered the letters PRIN . . . . ROSAL . . . and then came a great rent. As for the shoe, what was she to do with one poor, little tootsey sandal? The string was still fastened to it, so she hung it round her neck.

"Won't you give me a pair of shoes to go out in the snow, mum, if you please, mum?" cried the poor child.

"No, you wicked beast!" says Gruffanuff, driving her along with the poker, driving her down the cold stairs, driving her through the cold hall, flinging her out into the cold street so that the knocker, itself, shed tears to see her! But a kind fairy made the soft snow warm for her little feet and she wrapped herself up in the ermine of her mantle and was gone!

"And now let us think about breakfast," says the greedy Queen.

Nine o'clock came and they were all in the breakfast room and no Prince Bulbo as yet. The urn was hissing, the muffins were smoking, the eggs were done, there was a pot of raspberry jam and coffee and a beautiful chicken on the sideboard and the cook brought in the sausages. Oh, how nice they smelled!

"Where is Bulbo?" said the King. At this moment Glumboso entered with Captain Hedzoff, both looking very much disturbed.

"I am afraid, Your Majesty . . ." cries Glumboso.

"No business before breakfast, Glum," says the King. "Breakfast first, business next. Mrs. V., some more sugar!"

"Sire, I am afraid if we wait till after breakfast it will be too late," says Glumboso. "He–he–he'll be hanged at half-past nine."

"Don't talk about hanging and spoil my breakfast, you unkind, vulgar man," cries the Princess. "Pray, who is to be hanged?"

"Sire, it is the Prince," whispers Glumboso to the King.

"Talk about business after breakfast, I tell you!" says His Majesty, quite sulky.

"We shall have a war, Sire, depend on it," says the Minister. "His father, King Padella . . ."

THE TREASURE CHEST

"King who?" says the King. "Padella is not Giglio's father."

"It's Prince Bulbo they are hanging, Sire, not Prince Giglio," says the Prime Minister.

"You told me to hang the Prince, and I took the ugly one!" says Hedzoff. "I didn't think your Majesty intended to murder your own flesh-and-blood!"

The King, for all reply, flung the plate of sausages at Hedzoff's head. The Princess cried "Hee–karee–karee!" and fell down in a fainting fit.

"Turn the cock of the urn upon Her Royal Highness," said the King, and the boiling water gradually revived her.

His Majesty looked at his watch. "The question is," said he, "am I fast or slow? If I'm slow, we may as well go on with breakfast. If I'm fast, there is just the possibility of saving Prince Bulbo."

"A hundred-thousand plagues upon you! Can't you see that while you're talking my Bulbo is being hung?" screamed the Princess.

"By Jove! She's always right!" said the King, looking at his watch again. "There go the drums! What a deuced awkward thing!"

"Oh, papa, you goose! Write the reprieve and let me run with it," cries the Princess. And she got a sheet of paper and pen and ink.

"Confound it! Where are my spectacles?" the monarch exclaimed. At last the spectacles were got, and the King mended his pen and signed the reprieve, and Angelica ran with it as swift as the wind.

"You'd better stay, my love, and finish the muffins. There's no use going. Be sure it's too late," said the monarch. "Hand me over the raspberry jam!"

Angelica ran and ran. She ran through the market place and over the bridge and round the square and she came—she came to the *Execution Place* where she saw Bulbo laying his head on the block. The executioner raised his axe; but, at that moment, the Princess came up panting and cried, "Reprieve! Reprieve!"

Up the scaffold stairs she sprang and, flinging herself into Bulbo's arms, she cried, "O my Prince, my love! Thine Angelica has come in time to save thy precious existence!"

"I tell you what it is, Angelica," said Bulbo. "Since I came here yesterday, there has been such a row and disturbance and quarrelling and chopping off of heads, that I am inclined to go back to Crim Tartary."

"But with me as thy bride, my Bulbo!"

"Well, well, I suppose we must be married," said Bulbo. "But in the name of peace, do let us go back to breakfast."

Bulbo had carried in his mouth, all the time of the dismal ceremony, the fairy rose which his mother had told him never to part with. He had kept it between his teeth, even when he laid his poor head upon the block; but, as he spoke to Angelica, he forgot about the rose and, of course, it dropped out of his mouth. The romantic Princess stooped and seized it.

"Sweet rose," she exclaimed, "that bloomed upon my Bulbo's lips, never will I part from thee!" and she placed it in her bosom.

Then they went back to breakfast, and it appeared to Bulbo that Angelica became more lovely every moment. Strange to say, it was Angelica now who didn't care about him. It seemed to her he was not handsome any more. She thought they might postpone the marriage, but King Valoroso roared: "Pooh, stuff!" in a terrible voice. "We'll have no more shilly-shallying! Call the Archbishop and let the Prince and Princess be married offhand!"

THE TREASURE CHEST

Now, during this time Betsinda wandered on and on, on the great Crim Tartary road. An empty cart came by and the driver, seeing a pretty girl trudging along with bare feet, good-naturedly gave her a seat. He said he lived at the edge of the forest, where his old father was a woodman; and, if she liked, he would take her so far on her road.

Evening came, and all the black pines were bending with snow, and there, at last, was the comfortable light beaming in the woodman's windows. So they arrived and went into his cottage. He was an old man and had a number of children who were just at supper, with nice hot bread and milk. They jumped up and clapped their hands; and, when they saw the pretty stranger, they ran to her and brought her to the fire and rubbed her poor little feet and brought her bread and milk.

"Look, father," they said, "see what pretty, cold feet she has! And see what an odd cloak she has, just like the bit of velvet, that hangs up in our cupboard, which you found that day the cubs were killed by King Padella in the forest. And look, she has round her neck just such another little shoe as that you brought home and have shown us so often—a little, blue-velvet shoe!"

"What's all this about a shoe and a cloak?" said the woodman.

Then Betsinda explained that she had been left, when quite a little child, with this cloak and this shoe. She remembered having been in a forest and having lived in a cave with lions, and before that, in a fine house, as fine as the King's in town.

When the woodman heard this, he was astonished. He went to his cupboard and took out
of a stocking a five-shilling piece of King Cavolfiore and vowed it was exactly like the young
woman. And then he produced the shoe and
piece of velvet and compared them with the
things which Betsinda wore. In Betsinda's little
shoe was written, "Hopkins, maker to the Royal Family." So
in the other shoe was written, "Hopkins, maker to the Royal
Family." In the inside of Betsinda's piece of cloak was embroidered "PRIN . . . ROSAL . . . ," and in the other piece of
cloak was embroidered ". . . CESS . . . BA No. 246." So that,
when put together, you read PRINCESS ROSALBA No. 246. On
seeing this, the dear old woodman fell down on his knee, saying,
"O my Princess, O my rightful Queen of Crim Tartary! I hail
thee! I do thee homage!" And he rubbed his venerable nose three
times on the ground and put the Princess's foot on his head.

"Why," said she, "my good woodman, you must be a nobleman
of my royal father's Court!" For under the name of Betsinda,
Her Majesty, Rosalba, Queen of Crim Tartary, had read of the
customs of all foreign courts and nations.

"Lord Spinachi, once," said the good old man, "the humble
woodman these fifteen years, since the tyrant Padella dismissed me."

"First Lord of the Toothpick and Joint Keeper of the Snuffbox,
I mind me!" said Betsinda. "Thou heldest these posts under our
royal Sire. They are restored to thee! Rise, Marquis of Spinachi!"
And with indescribable majesty, the Queen, who had no sword
handy, waved the pewter spoon with which she had been taking
her bread and milk over the bald head of the old nobleman, whose
tears made a puddle on the ground and whose children went to
bed that night Lords and Ladies Bartolomeo, Ubaldo, Catarina,
and Ottavia degli Spinachi!

The old Marquis of Spinachi said that the whole country

groaned under Padella's tyranny and longed to return to its rightful sovereign. And late as it was, he sent his children, who knew the forest well, to summon this nobleman and that. So Her Majesty's followers gathered and they made her a crown of gilt paper and a robe of cotton velvet. And there came to her service, a powerful warrior by the name of Count Hogginarmo whose helmet was so large it took two strong negroes to carry it. Rosalba felt afraid of him even while he knelt before her. His eyes scowled at her from between his whiskers which grew clear up to them.

"Madame," he said, "my hand is free. I offer it, my heart and my sword to your service. My three wives lie buried in my ancestral vaults. Deign to be mine and I swear to bring to your bridal table the head of King Padella and the eyes and nose of his son, Prince Bulbo."

"Oh, Sir!" Rosalba said, withdrawing her hand in fright. "Your Lordship is exceedingly kind; but I am already attached to a young gentleman named Prince Giglio and never can I marry anyone but him."

Who can describe Hogginarmo's wrath at this remark?

Rising up from the
ground, he ground his
teeth and said, "R–r–re-
jected! The bold Hoggin-
armo rejected! All the
world shall hear of my
rage! And, you, Madam,
you above all shall rue
it!" And kicking the two
negroes before him, he
rushed away—his whisk-
ers streaming in the wind.

In another half-hour
he cut, slashed, banged
his way through the
army of poor Rosalba and took the Queen a prisoner. "Get a
horse van," he said to his grooms. "Clap the hussy into it and
send her with my compliments to His Majesty, King Padella!" So
this poor Queen was driven to Padella and thrust into a dungeon.

Meantime, the idea of marrying such an old creature as Gruffanuff had so frightened Prince Giglio, that he had packed his
trunks and taken an early coach out of Paflagonia. When they
stopped to change horses at Blomboginga, a very ordinary-looking
young woman with a bag under her arm asked for a place in the
coach. All the inside places were taken, and the young woman
was informed that she must go up on the roof. But the poor
woman coughed very much and Giglio pities her.

"I will give up my place to her," said he. Then he sprang up
gaily on to the roof of the diligence. A traveller got out at the
next station; so Giglio went inside and talked to the person next
him. She appeared to be a well-informed and entertaining female
and she gave Giglio all sorts of things out of the bag she carried—
cold fowl, slices of ham, and a most delicious piece of plum-pudding.

THE TREASURE CHEST

As they travelled, this queer woman talked to Giglio on a variety of subjects in which the poor Prince showed his ignorance. He owned, with many blushes, how ignorant he was, on which the lady said, "My dear Gigl..., my good young man, you have plenty of time before you. You have nothing to do but to improve yourself. Who knows but that you may find use for your knowledge someday, when .... when you may be wanted at home!"

"Good heavens, Madam!" says Giglio. "Do you know me?"

"I know a number of funny things," says the lady. "I advise you to stay at the town, where the coach stops, for the night. Stay there and study; and, when you want anything, look in this bag which I leave you."

"And to whom shall I be grateful, Madam," says Giglio.

"To the Fairy Blackstick," says the lady, flying out of the window. Giglio thought he had been dreaming. But there was the bag which Blackstick had given him; and, when he came to the town, he took it in his hand. Now this town where Giglio arrived was the celebrated university town of Bosforo. Giglio took lodgings opposite the Schools and, when he opened his trunk which the day before he had filled with his clothes, he found it contained only books. And in his bag, when Giglio looked in it, he found a student's cap and gown, a writing-book, an inkstand, pens, and a dictionary which was very useful to him as his spelling had been sadly neglected.

So Giglio sat down and worked away very hard for a year. One day, after the examinations, as he was diverting himself at a coffee-house with two friends, he chanced to look in the Bosforo Chronicle and read off quite easily (for he could read and write the longest words now) the following: 'Romantic Circumstance—It will be remembered that when the present revered sovereign of Crim Tartary, His Majesty King Padella, took possession of the throne, after having vanquished the late King Cavolfiore, that Prince's only child, the Princess Rosalba, was not found in the royal palace; and, it was said, had strayed into the forest where she had been eaten up by lions. Remains of a cloak and a shoe were found in the forest during a hunting-party. And these interesting relics of an innocent, little creature were kept by their finder, the Baron Spinachi, formerly an officer in Cavolfiore's household.

'Last Tuesday week, Baron Spinachi and a number of gentlemen attached to the former dynasty appeared in arms, crying, "God save Rosalba, Queen of Crim Tartary!" and surrounding a lady whom report describes as "beautiful exceedingly." This personage states that she was left in the Palace Garden of Blombodinga, where Her Royal Highness, the Princess Angelica, with *that elegant benevolence* which has always distinguished the heiress of the throne of Paflagonia, gave the little outcast a *shelter and a home!* She was educated in the Palace in a menial capacity, under the name of Betsinda. But she did not give satisfaction and was dismissed, carrying with her part of a mantle and a shoe, which she had on when first found. On the very same morning when she left, Prince Giglio, nephew to the King of Paflagonia, also quitted Blombodinga and has not been heard of since!"

'Second Edition, Express—We hear that the troop under Baron Spinachi has been utterly routed, by General Count Hogginarmo, and the *soidisant* Princess is sent a prisoner to the capital.'

"My good friends," said Giglio when he had finished reading, "disguise is henceforth useless. I am that Giglio. And I saw in Betsinda . . . . Rosalba . . . . the blushing sum of all perfection."

The Prince and his friends hastened home, highly excited by

the intelligence. Giglio went to his bag, opened it, and what do you think he found? A splendid, gold-handled sword and on the sheath was embroidered "ROSALBA FOR EVER!" And now his trunk opened with a sudden pong, and out there came a shining steel helmet; a cuirass; a pair of spurs; finally a complete suit of armour. The books on Giglio's shelves were all gone. Where there had been dictionaries, Giglio's friends found helmets, breast plates,

swords, etc.; and that evening, three cavaliers might have been seen issuing from the gates of Bosforo. They never drew bridle until they reached the last town on the frontier before you come to Crim Tartary. Here they stopped and refreshed at an hostel. As they were drinking, the market place filled with soldiers, and Giglio, looking forth, recognized the Paflagonian banners.

"It is my friend, my gallant Captain Hedzoff," Giglio cried. "Ho, Hedzoff! Whither march my Paflagonians?"

Hedzoff's head fell. "My Lord," he said, "we march as the allies of great Padella, Crim Tartary's monarch."

"Crim Tartary's usurper! Crim Tartary's grim tyrant," said the Prince on the balcony quite sarcastically. And stepping well-

forward, the royal youth delivered a speech so magnificent that no report can do justice to it. It lasted for three days and three nights, during which not a single person who heard him was tired, or remarked the difference between daylight and dark. At the end of this extraordinary effort, Captain Hedzoff flung up his helmet and cried, "Hurray! Hurray! Long live King Giglio!"

Meantime, as King Padella was a widower, he went to his captive, Rosalba, and offered to marry her that instant, but she declined his invitation in her usual polite, gentle manner—stating that Prince Giglio was her love. Uttering awful imprecations, His Majesty bade her prepare for death on the following morning. Cutting off her head was much too easy a death. He bethought himself of a pair of fierce lions which had lately been sent to him and he determined to hunt poor Rosalba down with these ferocious beasts. The lions were kept in a cage and their roaring might be heard over the whole city, the inhabitants of which thronged in numbers to see a poor young lady gobbled up by wild beasts.

The Princess was brought out in her nightgown, with all her beautiful hair falling down her back and looking so pretty, that even the keepers of the wild

animals wept plentifully at seeing her. And now the gates were
opened and with a wurrawarru-
rawarar, two great, lean, hungry
lions rushed out of their den. But
O, strange event! When the lions
came to Rosalba, instead of de-
vouring her with their great teeth,
it was with kisses they gobbled
her up. They seemed to say:

"Dear sister, don't you recollect your brothers in the forest?" And
she put her white arms round their tawny necks and kissed them.

King Padella was astonished. Count Hogginarmo was disgusted.

"Pooh," the Count said, "these lions are tame beasts! I believe
they are little boys dressed up in door-mats!"

"Ho," said the King, "you dare say this to your sovereign!
These are no lions, aren't they? My bodyguard, take Count Hogginarmo and fling him into the circus. Let him fight these lions!"

The haughty Hogginarmo looked scowling around. "Your
Majesty thinks Hogginarmo is afraid?" he said. "No, not of a
hundred-thousand lions!" And he jumped down into the circus.
Wurra wurra wurra wur-aw-aw-aw!!!
In about two minutes
The Count Hogginarmo was
GOBBLED UP
by
those lions,
bones, boots, and all,
and
There was an
End of him.

"Serves him right," said the King, "and now as the lions won't
eat that young woman, let the beef-eaters chop her into pieces!"

There was a dead silence then, which was broken by a Pang-arang–pang, pankarangkang and a knight and a herald rode in at the further end of the circus.

"Ha," exclaimed the King, "by my fay, 'tis the gallant Captain Hedzoff! What news from Paflagonia, gallant Hedzoff?"

The herald took a sheet of paper out of his hat and began to read: 'Know all men by these presents, that we, Giglio, King of Paflagonia, Sovereign Prince of Turkey and the Sausage Islands, having assumed our rightful throne and title, long time falsely borne by our usurping Uncle, styling himself King of Paflagonia...'

"Ha!" growled Padella.

'Hereby summon the false traitor, Padella, calling himself King of Crim Tartary....'

The King's curses were dreadful.

'. . . . to release from cowardly imprisonment his rightful sovereign, Rosalba, Queen of Crim Tartary, and restore her to her royal throne; in default of which, I, Giglio, proclaim the said Padella, sneak, traitor, humbug, usurper, and coward. I challenge him to meet me, with fists or with pistols, alone or at the head of his army, and will prove my words upon his wicked body!'

"Is that all?" said Padella, with the terrific calm of concentrated fury. "And what says my brother of Paflagonia to this rubbish?"

"The King's uncle hath been deprived of the crown he unjustly wore," said Hedzoff. "After the battle of Bombardaro, his whole army came over to our side, with the exception of Prince Bulbo."

"Ah! my boy, my boy, my Bulbo was no traitor!" cried Padella.

"Prince Bulbo, far from coming over to us, ran away, sir; but I caught him," said Hedzoff. "The Prince is a prisoner in our army, and terrific tortures await him if a hair of Princess Rosalba's head is injured."

"Do they?" exclaimed the furious Padella, who was now perfectly livid with rage. "Ho, torturers! Light up the fires and make the pincers hot! Get lots of boiling lead! *Bring out Rosalba!*"

THE TREASURE CHEST

Instantly Captain Hedzoff rode off to King Giglio's camp with news of the fate of Rosalba.

"The brutal ruthless ruffian, royal wretch!" Giglio exclaimed. "Go, some of you, and bring Prince Bulbo hither."

Bulbo was brought in chains, looking very uncomfortable.

"Oh, my poor Bulbo," said His Majesty, "hast thou heard the news? Thy brutal father has condemned Rosalba, p-p-put her to death!"

"What, killed Betsinda! Boo–hoo–hoo," cried out Bulbo.

And now think what must have been the feelings of the most *merciful of monarchs*, when he informed his prisoner that, in consequence of King Padella's *cruel and dastardly behaviour*, Prince Bulbo must be executed at eight o'clock next morning.

The noble Giglio could not restrain his tears. Prince Bulbo was taken back to his dungeon, where every attention was paid to him. The gaoler's wife sent him tea. The undertaker came and measured him for the handsomest coffin which money could buy—even this didn't console Bulbo. The cook brought him dishes which he once used to like; but he wouldn't touch them. He sat down and began writing an adieu to Angelica. Then he

217

got up on the top of a hatbox, on the top of a chair, on the top of his bed, on the top of his table, and looked out to see whether he might escape, as the clock kept always ticking. But, looking out of the window was one thing and jumping, another; and the town clock struck seven. So he got into bed for a little sleep, but the gaoler came and woke him and said, "Git up, Your Royal 'Ighness, if you please, it's *ten minutes to eight!*"

So poor Bulbo got up and he saw the soldiers who had come for him. "Lead on!" he said, and they led the way deeply affected. They came out into the square, and there was King Giglio come to take leave of Bulbo. His Majesty kindly shook hands with him, and the *gloomy procession* marched on—when hark!

THE TREASURE CHEST

Haw–wurraw–wurraw–aworr! A roar of wild beasts was heard. And who should come riding into the town, frightening away the boys but Rosalba! The fact is, the lions had made a dash at the open gate, gobbled up the beef-eaters in a jiffy; and away they went with Rosalba on the back of one of them, and they carried her, turn and turn about, till they came to the city where Prince Giglio's army was encamped.

When the King heard of the Queen's arrival, he rushed out of his breakfast-room to hand Her Majesty off her lion!

"Prince Bulbo is reprieved this time," he said and most graciously invited him to breakfast.

As soon as King Padella heard that his victim had escaped him, his fury knew no bounds. He ordered out his whole army. But King Giglio's advance guard kept him acquainted with the enemy's dealings, and he was in no wise disconcerted. On the contrary, he did everything to amuse and divert the Princess; gave her a most elegant breakfast, dinner, lunch, and got up a ball for her that evening. Dancing the twenty-fifth polka with Rosalba, he remarked with wonder the ring she wore; then Rosalba told him how she had got it from Gruffanuff, who no doubt had picked it up when Angelica flung it away.

"Yes," says the Fairy Blackstick, who had come to see the young people, "that ring I gave Giglio's mother; it is enchanted, and whoever wears it, looks beautiful in the eyes of the world."

"Rosalba needs no ring, I am sure," says Giglio. "She is beautiful enough, in my eyes, without any enchanted aid."

"Oh, Sir!" said Rosalba.

"Take off the ring and try," said the King and drew the ring off her finger. In *his* eyes she looked just as handsome as before.

"Bulbo, my poor lad! Come and try on this ring," said the King. "The Princess Rosalba makes it a present to you."

No sooner had Bulbo put it on, but lo and behold, he appeared an agreeable young Prince enough; and the Fairy Blackstick said, "Now you see what I said from the first, that a little misfortune has done you good. YOU, Giglio, had you been bred in prosperity, would scarcely have learned to read or write. You would have been idle and extravagant, and could not have been a good King as now you will be. You, Rosalba, would have been so flattered, that your head might have been turned like Angelica's."

"Oh, you, you darling!" says Giglio to Rosalba, and he was just holding out his arms in order to give her a hug when a messenger came rushing in and said, "My Lord, the enemy!"

"To arms!" cries Giglio.

"Oh, mercy!" says Rosalba and fainted, of course.

He snatched one kiss from her lips and rushed forth to the field of battle! Fine blows are struck, dreadful wounds delivered! Bugles blow, drums beat, horses neigh, fifes sing, soldiers roar! In a word, the overthrow of King Padella was complete.

"Do you acknowledge Rosalba as your rightful Queen and give up

the crown and treasures?" asked Giglio.

"If I must, I must," said Padella, who was naturally very sulky.

And they tied his hands behind him, and bound his legs tight under his horse, having set him with his face to the tail; and he was led back to King Giglio's quarters and thrust into a dungeon.

All was now joy in King Giglio's circle. Dancing, feasting, fun, illuminations, and jollifications of all sorts ensued. *Their Majesties* were never separated during the whole day, but breakfasted, dined, and supped together. It was agreed they should be married as soon as they reached the capital, and orders were dispatched to the Archbishop of Blombodinga to hold himself in readiness to perform the interesting ceremony. Duke Hedzoff carried the message; and, immediately, he seized Glumboso, the Ex-Prime Minister, and made him refund that considerable sum of money which the old scoundrel had secreted out of the late King's treasure. He also clapped Valoroso into prison. So these two Ex-Royal personages were sent for a year to the House of Correction.

The Fairy Blackstick, as they were riding in triumphal progress toward Giglio's capital, exhorted him to deal justly by his subjects and never break his promise when he had once given it.

"Why is Fairy Blackstick always warning me to keep my word? Does she suppose I'm not a man of honour?" asks Giglio testily.

When the Royal party arrived at the last stage before you reach Blombodinga, who should be in waiting, in her carriage there, but the Princess Angelica! She rushed into her husband's arms and had no eyes but for Bulbo, who appeared perfectly lovely to her on account of the fairy ring which he wore; whilst she herself, wearing the magic rose in her bonnet, seemed entirely beautiful to the enraptured Bulbo. A splendid luncheon was served, of which all our friends partook.

"What can have induced that hideous old Gruffanuff to dress up in such an absurd way?" says Giglio to Rosalba. And a figure of fun Gruffy certainly was. She was dressed in a white silk dress with lace over, a wreath of white roses on her wig, a lace veil, and her yellow old neck was covered with diamonds. She ogled the King in such a manner that His Majesty burst out laughing.

"We must be at church before twelve," sighs out Gruffanuff in a languishing voice, hiding her old face behind her fan.

"And then I shall be the happiest man in my dominions," cries Giglio, with an elegant bow to the blushing Rosalba.

"Oh, my Giglio!" exclaims Gruffanuff. "Can it be that this happy moment at length has arrived and I am about to become the enraptured bride of my adored Giglio? Lend me a smelling bottle, somebody. I certainly shall faint with joy."

"YOU my bride?" roars out Giglio.

"YOU marry my Prince?" cried poor little Rosalba.

"Pooh! Nonsense! The woman's mad!" exclaimed the King.

"I should like to know who else is going to be married, if I am not?" shrieked Gruffanuff. "Has not Prince Giglio promised to marry his Barbara? Is not this Giglio's signature?" And she handed the Archbishop the document the Prince had signed.

"H'm'," said the Archbishop, "the document is certainly a–a document."

"Is it your handwriting, Giglio?" cried the Fairy Blackstick.

"Y–y–y–es," poor Giglio gasps out, "I had forgotten the confounded paper. Help the Queen, someone—Her Majesty has fainted." But Gruffanuff flung her arms round the Archbishop's neck and bellowed out, "Justice, justice, my Lord Chancellor!"

"Won't you take that sum of money which Glumboso hid," said Giglio; "two-hundred-and-eighteen-thousand millions?"

"I will have that and you, too!" said Gruffanuff.

"Let us throw the crown jewels into the bargain," gasps Giglio.

"I will wear them by my Giglio's side!" said Gruffanuff.

Giglio was half-mad with rage by this time. "I will not marry her," says he. "Oh, Fairy, Fairy, give me counsel!"

" 'Why is Fairy Blackstick always warning me to keep my word? Does she suppose that I am not a man of honour?' " said the Fairy, quoting Giglio's own haughty words. He quailed under the brightness of her eyes: there was no escape from that.

"Well," said he in a dreadful voice, "Countess, let us be married. I can keep my word, but I can die afterwards."

"Oh, dear Giglio," cries Gruffanuff skipping up, "I knew, I knew I could trust thee!"

Rosalba did not faint again. Though she loved Giglio more than her life, she was determined, as she told the Fairy, not to cause him to break his royal word.

"I cannot marry him, but I shall love him always," says she.

So the Fairy kissed Rosalba with peculiar tenderness.

Before the ceremony at church, it was the custom in Paflagonia for the bride and bridegroom to sign the Contract of Marriage. So the party drove to the palace. Rosalba stepped out of her coach, supported by Bulbo, and stood almost fainting, to have a last look of her dear Giglio. As for Blackstick, she was now standing at the palace door. Giglio came up the steps with his horrible bride on his arm, looking as pale as if he was going to execution.

"Are you determined to make this poor young man unhappy?" says Blackstick.

"To marry him, yes! What business is it of yours?" cries Gruffanuff.

"You won't take the money he offered you?"

"No!"

"You won't let him off his bargain, though you know you cheated him when you made him sign the paper?"

"Impudence! Policemen, remove this woman!" cries Gruffanuff. The policemen were rushing forward, but with a wave of her wand the Fairy struck them all like so many statues in their places.

"You won't take anything in exchange for your bond?" cries the Fairy, with awful severity. "I speak for the last time."

"No!" shrieks Gruffanuff stamping with her foot. "I'll have my husband, my husband, my husband!"

"YOU SHALL HAVE YOUR HUSBAND!" the Fairy Blackstick cried; and advancing a step, laid her hand on the nose of the

KNOCKER. As she touched it, the brass nose seemed to elongate; the eyes rolled wildly; the arms and legs uncurled themselves; the knocker expanded *into* a figure in yellow livery, six-feet high; and Jenkins Gruffanuff once more trod the threshold off which he had been lifted more than twenty years ago!

"Master's not at home," says Jenkins, just in his old voice; and Mrs. Jenkins, giving a dreadful youp, fell down in a fit, in which nobody minded her. For everybody was shouting: "Huzzay! Huzzay! Long live the King and Queen!" The bells were ringing, the guns roaring. Bulbo was embracing everybody; the Lord Chancellor was flinging up his wig and shouting like a madman; Hedzoff had got the Archbishop round the waist, and they were dancing a jig; and, as for Giglio, I leave you to imagine what he was doing. If he kissed Rosalba once, twice, twenty-thousand times, I'm sure I don't think he was wrong. So Gruffanuff opened the hall door with a low bow, just as he had been accustomed to do; and they all went in and signed the book, and then they went to church and were married, and the Fairy Blackstick sailed away on her cane, and was never more heard of in Paflagonia.